These crazy characters are
GOIN' COCONUTS

Professor Kruse—A criminal mastermind with a Prussian accent, a foul temper, and a fierce determination to obtain a shell necklace, last seen around Marie Osmond's lovely neck.

Webster—A soft-spoken hit man who's guilty of kidnapping, murder, extortion, and hit-and-run driving . . . and that's just in the first five minutes of the movie.

Mr. Wong—A menacing millionaire who keeps a Venus's-flytrap as a housepet and equips a jet ski with a bomb . . . aimed at Donny and Marie.

Tricia—She's blond and beautiful, but is she after Marie's necklace or Donny's heart?

Sid—As Donny and Marie's manager, he's protected them from over-eager fans and kept them supplied with their favorite toothpaste. But he never expected anything like this.

Donny and Marie—They play themselves in this wacky adventure. They're marked for murder. But if they're going to go down, they'll go down smiling.

THE LAUREL-LEAF LIBRARY brings together under a single imprint outstanding works of fiction and non-fiction particularly suitable for young adult readers, both in and out of the classroom. The series is under the editorship of Charles F. Reasoner, Professor of Elementary Education, New York University.

GOIN' COCONUTS

a novelization
by Vic Crume

based on the
screenplay by
William Mark Daniels
and
Raymond Harvey

LAUREL-LEAF LIBRARY

A Laurel-Leaf Library Edition
Published by
Dell Publishing Co., Inc.
1 Dag Hammarskjold Plaza
New York, New York 10017

Laurel-Leaf Library ® TM 766734, Dell Publishing Co., Inc.

ISBN: 0-440-92933-4

Printed in the United States of America
First printing—November 1978
Second printing—December 1978

GOIN' COCONUTS

CHAPTER 1

~~~~~~

WILD APPLAUSE FLOODED the big concert hall—a sound that usually made Donny and Marie's business manager a very happy man.

But for once, Sid was feeling anything but happy. Onstage, the two Osmonds kept right on laughing, bowing, blowing kisses to the fans just as though they didn't have a plane to catch and things to do—like taking off makeup, snatching up carryon airline bags and getting to the airport.

"No encores. Please!" Sid groaned. He checked and rechecked his watch, groaned louder and paced the wings in despair.

But that sad sound didn't reach Donny and

Marie. To Sid's dismay, he saw Donny signal the band. The dreaded encore began. "That does it!" Sid almost wept. "We'll never make the plane now. Goodbye, Hawaii!"

Loyal to their fans as they were, neither Donny nor Marie had any idea of saying "Goodbye, Hawaii" before they'd had the chance to call out "Aloha" to that beautiful fiftieth state. They came romping offstage, speeding past other performers and the technicians. "Come on, Sid!" Marie cried. "We don't want to be late!"

"Late! *You* don't want to be late! One encore wasn't enough. You had to do three!"

"The audience liked us," Donny grinned.

"And they pay our salaries," Marie chirped. "Yours, too, Sid," she added.

"So do the fans in Hawaii," Sid replied grumpily. "Hurry *up!*"

Twenty-three minutes before boarding time, a skycap was handing Sid a bunch of luggage stubs and a ticket envelope. "There you are, sir, all set. Your Hawaii Flight Ten leaves from Gate Twelve . . . and aloha!"

Marie grinned. "See, Sid? We'd have had time for *another* encore."

"And we still have time to call home and tell Mom we're on our way." Donny's dark eyes twinkled. "Per *schedule*," he added. "There's a phone booth just over there."

He reached the booth just a step ahead of a chubby little man wearing the round, white collar of a priest. Donny stepped back. "You first," he smiled.

"Bless you, my son," the black-clad, figure answered sweetly, entering the booth and snapping the door tight.

His gentle voice completely changed when he spoke into the phone. "Operator," he rasped. "Gimme Hawaii."

As Donny stood waiting a polite distance from the booth, a phone was ringing in a lavishly beautiful Hawaiian mansion. A burly man in a chauffeur' uniform answered. "Wong residence . . . Charley! Did you get it?"

"Did I get it! Mickey, I got it right here in my hand." Grinning, he glanced down at the necklace and pendant that sparkled in his plump, pink palm. "Yeah," he went on. "I'll be on Flight Ten. Some of Kruse's boys are on my tail, but I can handle 'em." He glanced through the glass door as Marie joined Donny. They both smiled warmly at him. He smiled back and kept on talking. "No. I can't speak louder. There's a couple of apple knockers hanging around outside this booth. Gimme the boss."

Mickey groaned. "You sure you gotta speak to him? He's out in the garden somewhere."

"Find 'im," Charley snapped. "And hurry it up, will ya? I got a problem."

Outside the booth, Donny was beginning to wish he hadn't been so nicely brought up. That call was taking a long time. He glanced around the busy terminal. "Guess we'll have a quiet trip," he sighed. "Nobody's recognized us, nobody wants autographs. It'll be real nice for a change."

Marie nodded understandingly. "Yep, I hate it, too."

Donny suddenly perked up. "Well, that's all about to change," he murmured. "Look who's coming!"

Marie glanced around to see a tall, beautiful girl heading their way. "Why, Donny!" she murmured, "I didn't know you had *older* fans. Twenty-five if she's a day."

"Just you wait," her brother whispered back.

"For how long?" Marie giggled as the "older fan" sailed right past Donny and on toward the phone booth. She stopped, turned back, and glanced at Donny.

"Hi," he said pleasantly. "Phone's in use, I guess."

The beautiful creature barely nodded. Swiftly she walked away.

"Killer!" Marie whispered, and tried to muffle a loud giggle. She looked over toward the phone booth. "Gosh! He's putting in more money."

Coins were still clanging in the slot when Mickey finally spotted his employer on the garden hilltop terrace. Mr. Wong's trusted bodyguard, J. L., was watching the villainous-looking Wong circle a target dummy representing an ancient Japanese samurai warrior. Wong's sword flashed in the sunlight, and down rolled the samurai's head.

"Mr. Wong," Mickey called out, dragging the nearly endless phone cord up over the rocks. "Phone call for you, Mr. Wong."

Mr. Wong didn't bother to turn his head. "*I* didn't hear it ring," he said coldly.

"It's Charley, Mr. Wong," Mickey panted, handing over the phone. "We got the necklace."

Mr. Wong did not bother to speak to the faraway Charley. "Excellent," he said. "Then we have beaten Professor Kruse. You two arrange to meet Charley at the airport." He handed back the phone and strolled away, leaving an unhappy Mickey to reel in the yards of phone cord stretching back to the mansion.

Long before Mickey had completed that journey, Charley sighed in disappointment and headed out of the phone booth. "He could have said something like, 'great work, Charley,'" he muttered, walking away sadly without a glance or a thank-you to the patiently-waiting Osmonds.

Marie looked puzzled. "What a sweet little man," she said, watching him walk away. "We should have asked him if he's lost or anything. He seems so helpless."

"If we don't get a call through to Mom, she'll think *we're* lost and helpless. Come on."

Marie turned away and followed her brother to the phone booth. If she hadn't, she would have seen a strange sight—the "helpless" little man being jumped by two thugs. Swiftly, he dealt them a series of quick, deadly chops. Then, not even out of breath, he neatly piled them on a nearby luggage cart, and went calmly on his way. Two amazed luggage attendants, the only witnesses, were too stunned to move. "He must have gone to Notre Dame," one whispered, awestruck, to the other.

"At *least*," his fellow worker whispered back. "Man! Did you see that speed!"

Charley, his priestly attire neat as a pin, went briskly on his way toward Gate Twelve.

At the phone booth, Sid came rushing up. "Come on, kids. Come on!"

Donny nodded. "Have to go now, Mom, he said, "Give our love to Dad . . . and Jay . . . and Merrill . . . and Jimmy."

Marie leaned forward. "And to Wayne . . . and Alan . . ."

"And Virgil," Donny cut in. "And Tom . . . and Uncle Bruce and Aunt Ida."

Sid rolled his eyes toward the ceiling. "Other managers," he muttered, "they got *people* for clients. Me, I get the state of Utah."

Up ahead, Charley, on his way to Gate Twelve, suddenly stopped, terror spreading across his round, innocent-looking face. Standing by the boarding gate and giving every boarding passenger a close, deadly stare, was a sinister-looking man. "Webster!" Charley gasped. He shrunk back and clutched the necklace tucked in his pocket. "What'll I do!"

He was saved by a sudden cry. "It's Donny and Marie!" a fan cried out.

Instantly, a group of teenagers came out of nowhere and surrounded the Osmonds. And it was an inspiration to Charley! Almost as quickly as the fans had appeared, Charley became a member of the group. Roughly, he brushed everybody aside, but managed to keep his voice gentle. "Excuse me, my children," he said softly.

Donny and Marie smiled. Charley wasted no time. "You see," he began, "the little ones of my church all contributed pennies to send me to Hawaii. And then when they heard you were going on the same plane, they asked me to give you this."

Smiling, he quickly pressed the necklace into Marie's hand. Quickly, but not quickly enough to escape the sharp look of the same tall, pretty girl Donny had tried to fascinate at the telephone booth. She hardly heard the fat little man say, "It's in appreciation of all the pleasure you've given them."

"Oh, that's very sweet," Marie said, almost shyly. "But, really—I couldn't!"

Charley tried to look very sad. "I know it's not valuable," he murmured, "but—"

"That's not it!" Marie replied quickly. "It's just that—"

Charley smiled. "Then, please! Wear it . . . for good things and good music to come for the little orphans."

Marie and Donny exchanged glances. Even Sid looked sympathetic. He nodded and smiled at Marie.

"I'll keep it always," his star said softly. "Thank you."

"Thank *you!*" Charley exclaimed. "You don't know how much this means to—er, the little orphans."

"Here!" Sid pulled from his pocket autographed pictures of Donny and Marie. "Maybe you'd like to have these for the wife and kids."

The "priest" forgot to look shocked. He

beamed, said "Thank you," and hurried back along the corridor. Only one pair of eyes watched him head for a telephone booth—the eyes of Tricia, the tall girl Donny had admired. Then, looking away, she moved on toward the boarding gate, close behind Donny . . . and Marie.

CHAPTER 2

~~~~~~

FOR THE SECOND time within a half hour, Mickey was picking up the phone in the Wong residence and hearing Charley's voice. "Aw, no, Charley. Have a heart. The boss is way up there on the terrace."

But Charley was firm. "I got a problem. Get him, Mickey. And hurry. I gotta get on that plane in a minute."

"Okay. Gotcha."

Charley relaxed a bit and got his mind on exactly what he'd say to Mr. Wong. It would have to be short, fast, and made perfectly plain —"Get the necklace from the girl who looks like the boy she's with." Charley half smiled over the clever way he was outsmarting Webster!

"Well! How are ya, Charley?" a voice spoke loudly in his ear, but not from faraway Hawaii. A heavy hand jerked at his shoulder.

Charley spun around. "Webster!" he gasped. "Listen! I ain't got it! I swear."

Webster grinned. "Tsk! Tsk! And you, a priest, swearing a thing like that! Come on, Charley. Why don't we just get on the plane and talk it over, huh?"

No wonder Mr. Wong heard no one on the line when Mickey arrived with the telephone. "Nobody there," he said disgustedly.

"But it was Charley. Said he had a problem."

Mr. Wong shrugged and handed back the phone. "I hope not. For *his* sake," he said coldly.

By the time Webster and Charley were settled in their seats, Donny and Marie were already listening to music on the stereo earphones, and Sid was napping.

Marie giggled. "Hey, Donny!" She tapped her brother's arm. "Look. Here comes your dear old friend, Miss Iceberg."

Donny took one quick glance along the aisle then scrunched down. He frowned at Marie. No one could have been more surprised than Marie when Miss Iceberg came to a stop beside Donny's aisle seat. She smiled and it seemed, at least to Donny, that a billion kilowatts powered the smile the tall girl gave him.

"Hi!" she said warmly. "Enjoying the flight?"

The change was so sudden that Donny had the feeling she must be speaking to someone else. He looked quickly to left and right. "Er, yes, very much."

"So am I," Tricia said. She sat down right across the aisle and took out a book. But before she began reading she flashed another brilliant smile at him.

Without even looking at Donny, Marie knew her brother had suddenly grown ten feet tall and was wearing a smug look on his handsome face. She leaned close and whispered, "Donny, aren't you glad I was nice to that priest? He can marry you right on the plane."

She grinned. But Donny was too busy beaming back at Tricia to listen to his young sister.

A few rows back, one passenger was not enjoying his Hawaii-bound flight. Charley. He knew that nothing more than a plane ticket, baggage stubs, and a bunch of publicity photos of those kids were in the inner coat pocket that Webster was searching. But something told him there'd be trouble ahead. "I tell ya, Webster—I ain't got it. Take those stubs. You can go through my luggage, too."

"If you're faking it, Charley, they're going to bury you in that suit you're wearing. What's this?" He drew out the autographed pictures of the Osmonds. He stared at them. "Oh. Fan pictures."

Charley sighed in relief. "Webster, if I had it, you woulda found it on me." He leaned back and closed his eyes.

Up ahead, Marie looked from Sid to Donny. Sid was sleeping, the other concentrating on being ready to smile in case the beautiful creature across the aisle happened to look up from her book. Marie nudged her brother. "Donny— help me fasten this necklace, will you? I'm going back and show that nice priest I'm wearing it and thank him again."

"Good idea. And tell him to thank the orphans, too."

As she made her way along the aisle, Charley opened his eyes—to a horrible sight. The necklace! Marie, smiling, was fluffing it up in her fingers as she came closer. Charley knew that when Webster saw it, one thing was almost for sure—there'd be only seconds to live. He squeezed his eyes shut, almost stopped breathing, hands clenched over his chest.

Marie hesitated as she bent toward him, the necklace swinging in plain sight, then at that moment the FASTEN YOUR SEAT BELTS sign flashed on. She turned away. Only a split second later, Webster looked up from tucking Charley's luggage stubs and the fan pictures into his wallet. He glanced at Charley. "Say, I never saw a guy so scared of flying." He shook his head. "I'll get you a cup of water."

Donny, seeing Marie walking back, stood up in the aisle to let her pass. "That was quick," he said.

Marie sighed. "I decided I'd be bothering him. He looked like he was praying. Besides, the FASTEN BELTS sign came on."

"Oh." Donny looked out over the magnificent fields of cloud mist. "Guess we'll be landing soon. You can thank him then."

"That's what I plan to do," Marie replied, looking bored with that free advice.

Back beside Charley, Webster sat down again and handed Charley a small cup. "Here y'are."

"Thanks." Charley sipped the water.

"Ya know, Charley," Webster took the Osmonds' picture from his wallet. "Something's been bothering me. Why you got these pictures?"

Charley tried to chuckle. "Aw, they were giving 'em out at the airport."

"The Osmonds, huh? Donny and Marie Osmond. And they're right on this plane, aren't they . . . right up there?"

Charley yawned. "I didn't notice."

Webster stared at the pictures. He nodded. "They're nice, clean-cut kids."

A gong sounded and the FASTEN SEAT BELTS lighted up again. Charley heaved a giant sigh.

"Guess we're ready to land." He gulped down the last of the water and fumbled for the seat belt.

Webster stopped him. "Charley—let me save you a little trouble. Don't bother with the seat belt."

"But—"

"You won't be needing it. You see, Charley—I know you've crossed me. It isn't nice to make an old friend look bad, Charley."

Charley's eyes widened. "You mean . . . ?"

Webster smiled. "I mean. You know what they say—'when you travel, don't drink the water.'"

Charley sank back, and that moment, Marie Osmond lost her chance to say thank you!

Sid, Donny, and Marie could never have landed anywhere on earth under more beautiful skies—a fact that didn't seem to take Sid's mind off his job.

He hurried them along. "Now you've got to meet reporters and photographers. It'll take just a minute. You wait here a sec."

As he rushed off, Tricia walked over to them. "It was so nice talking to you."

"*Smiling* to you," Marie almost said aloud, but didn't. "Same here," she replied.

Donny grinned. "Uh—where will you be staying, Tricia?"

"I hadn't really decided," Tricia beamed.

"We'll be at the Royal Hawaiian," Donny announced.

Silently, Marie formed the words—*that sounds nice, maybe I'll stay there too.*

Sure enough! Tricia nodded. "That sounds nice, maybe I'll stay there too."

Sid's arrival kept Marie from exploding in one giant giggle. "Go on in, kids," he said, "I'll see about the luggage."

"Sid, couldn't we wait a minute?" Marie asked. She touched the necklace. "I wanted to thank the priest."

"No time," Sid answered. "Tell you what— maybe when he gets off the plane we can steer him over and get a publicity shot for the orphanage. How's that?"

"Oh, that'd be wonderful. Okay, let's go."

Tricia joined the group. Together they walked to the side door of the terminal building.

Mr. Wong's chauffeur, Mickey, and the tough bodyguard, J. L., watched the last few exiting passengers. "I'm sure Charley said Flight Ten. But I guess that one at the end is the last passenger."

"And he's sure not Charley," J. L. said.

Briskly, this very last one of Flight Ten's passengers strode past them. "*Webster!*" Mickey exclaimed in a whisper.

J. L. stared. "That . . . is not so good. . . .

Come on. Let's get over to the plane. Something's gone very wrong."

"Charley said he had a problem," Mickey said worriedly.

They hurried off.

One quick look at the slumped-down passenger inside the plane was all Mickey and J. L. needed to know Charley didn't have a problem anymore. "Let's get out of here!" Mickey gasped. "We gotta get that Webster."

"Yeah," J. L. agreed. "Mr. Wong won't like it if we don't."

In the terminal building Ito, Professor Kruse's henchman, watched Webster striding along. Ito was not the kind of person to get lost in a crowd, and Webster went straight toward him. Even though they both worked for Professor Kruse, Webster still shuddered at the sight of the menacing, sinister Ito every time he saw him.

Before he could speak Ito, in a voice hard as a concrete block, asked the important question. "You have it?" He eyed Webster unblinkingly.

Webster shook his head. "Charley stashed it somewhere."

Ito stared. "Professor Kruse is not going to like this."

Webster shrugged. "Neither is Mr. Wong." He held out Charley's baggage stubs. "Here. Check 'em out. They're for Charley's luggage."

"And Charley?" questioned Ito.

"Don't worry. He's already checked out." He grinned. "*I* checked *him* out."

Because of the crowd gathered around Donny and Marie, neither Mr. Wong's team nor Professor Kruse's spotted each other. But they didn't miss seeing the two good-looking young stars, now decked out in beautiful Hawaiian leis, smiling at the admiring circle around them.

As the last flashbulbs popped and photographers and reporters left, Tricia edged close to the laughing, nodding pair. She smiled. "Marie— can I ask you something?"

Marie's eyes sparkled. Tricia wasn't the first girl to ask Marie "something." She smiled back. "He's a Pisces, Tricia. And he won't be twenty till February. And—yes. Those are all caps. Okay?"

Donny glared, but Tricia's eyes sparkled just as brightly. "I wasn't going to ask you about teeth. About your necklace. Have you had it long? Is it a family heirloom?"

Marie's hand went to the pendant. "Oh! This necklace! No. A sweet little man gave it to me just before we boarded the plane. A priest. I wanted to thank him again here, but I guess I've missed my chance."

Necklace! J. L. and Mickey forgot about celebrities and stared, stunned, at Marie.

A short distance away, Webster pulled out the Osmond pictures. "That Charley!" he exclaimed angrily. "So that's what's happened to the necklace!"

But there was no time to lose in thinking about Charley, and Webster knew it. What I *can't* lose now," he muttered, "are those Osmonds. I gotta get a car *fast*."

J. L. and Mickey had already figured that out. By the time Sid was getting his charges to the limousine, J. L.'s car was humming and ready to go.

Blissfully unaware that they had attracted rather unusual fans, Donny stopped at the limousine door and gazed at the soft, tropical view. "Let's take the scenic drive," he sighed. "Hawaii! Doesn't it do something to you, Sid?"

"It won't do anything *for* me unless the concert's a sell-out. Get in the car, kids."

"Come on, Sid," Marie laughed, climbing in after Donny. "This place is beautiful. All those palm trees. All those coconuts. You *gotta* love it."

Sid slammed the door shut. "I'd 'gotta love it' only if I were another coconut—which I'm not. But okay. Scenic drive, driver."

The big limousine glided smoothly forward. Marie sighed contentedly. "Hawaii is wonderful—whether or not you're a coconut. And I know we're going to have the most wonderful, relaxing time ever. I can feel it in my bones."

Nobody disagreed. Nobody, including Marie, knew her bones were sending out the wrong signals!

CHAPTER 3

J. L. AND MICKEY were already pulling away from the curb when Webster began the search for his own transportation.

Out of the corner of his eye he glimpsed the Osmond limousine glide past followed by a second car. Frantically he looked around for something available on wheels. To his delight a sedan, motor running, was almost under his nose. The rear trunk stood open and the owner was bending over the sidewalk picking up a heavy golf bag.

In a flash, Webster was in the driver's seat. He spun the wheels forward. At that very moment the car's owner pitched the golf bag—also forward. Off Webster went in a shower of clanking clubs.

But that was no noise at all compared with the grinding sound of a sideswipe as Webster tried to overtake the car between himself and the Osmonds. J. L. swerved and managed to keep Mr. Wong's car under control. Webster wasn't so lucky. He spun, skidded past parked cars, and square in front of a sign, OKAY DRIVING SCHOOL, wrecked his stolen transportation.

Mickey looked back. "Hey, J. L., that was Webster!" He grinned. "Well, he's out of it now."

J. L. grinned. "We got 'em all to ourselves. Looks like they're gonna take the scenic route to wherever they're headed. All the better for us!"

Far from being out of it, Webster was getting into it—this time into the training car of the Okay Driving School. The old lady "learner" on the front seat smiled over at him and put down her notebook and student driver's instruction manual. "Oh, you'll drive first?" she asked the school's newest instructor.

Webster did not bother to reply, so she bent over her notebook, jotting down helpful information on shifting gears and speedometer readings.

As Webster gathered top speed, she noted with interest that they were gaining on the car ahead. And she noted with even more interest that the car ahead was gaining on a big limousine ahead of *it*.

In the limousine Sid was in the mood to get on to the Royal Hawaiian. "Enough with the scenery," he said grumpily. "We'd better get to the hotel."

"Relax," Donny grinned. "It'll be good for your nerves."

Before Sid could even consider this advice, the limousine got a gentle nudge from Mr. Wong's car. "Hey! What was that?"

"Probably a rock in the road," Marie answered dreamily, gazing off toward a gorgeous hedge of pancake-size hibiscus blossoms. "Isn't that beautiful?"

Behind them J. L. dropped back slightly—just in time for Webster to come swirling up to try to crowd Mr. Wong's car off the road then drop back.

"Hey—who's that?" Mickey looked around. "'STUDENT LEARNER CAR. OKAY DRIVING SCHOOL.' Say! That's some student they got enrolled!"

Webster came roaring up for a second bash. This time his elderly passenger put down her notebook. "This must be an Advanced Student lesson," she remarked. "I think I should tell you I'm signed up for Beginning Driving."

Up ahead, Marie Osmond also noticed the strange antics of the Okay Driving School car.

"They teach a really crazy Driver's Ed here, don't they?"

As they rounded a curve, Marie was unable to give the others a real blow-by-blow of the traffic behind them. Webster really socked J. L. and Mickey out of contention. In triumph, he zoomed on to take on a new opponent—the Osmond limousine. Mr. Wong's car had nothing to do but wait for the wreckers.

"*Hey!*" Sid yelled as Webster came in for the kill.

"He's only a learner, Sid," Marie said kindly.

Sid leaned forward. "If you don't mind—the tour's over, driver. Take us to the hotel."

Instantly, their driver obliged. He swung the big car in a U-turn. Webster tried hard to follow, and after a skid, a stop, and a start, succeeded.

Sid and the Osmonds didn't notice Mr. Wong's smashed car or see J. L. and Mickey at a handy roadside telephone booth. But Webster, screaming along at top speed, saw the pair. Gaily, he waved to the foe—and, just as gaily, the Okay Driving School learner's car took the plunge! Off the road it went with Webster terrified and the old lady disgusted.

She stepped away from the wreck and straightened her hat. "It's been most interesting, but if you don't mind, sir, I'll walk back," said she. "I'll leave your driving brochures here on the seat." Off she stalked.

Webster didn't move a muscle. He couldn't.

Sid, glad to be getting back to work, stepped out of the limousine at the Royal Hawaiian entrance. "Okay. Let's get checked in. While you're unpacking, I'll arrange for the rehearsal rooms. And hurry it up, kids. We've got work to do."

"As though we could forget," Marie sighed. "But don't you forget, Sid—I'm really going to *explore* Hawaii."

Sid grinned. "Okay, Marie—as long as you explore the rehearsal hall first."

By the time J. L. and Mickey made it by taxi to the Royal Hawaiian, Donny and Marie were going over a new tune for their first Hawaiian performance.

Much to Donny's delight, but not Marie's, Tricia wandered in to listen.

"She's too old for you, Donny," his sister announced sternly.

"Come on, Marie, she's my age."

Marie sniffed. "Your age! Donny, she's old enough to be your mother." She looked across the room at Tricia. "Well—your older sister, anyway."

Donny grinned. "So maybe she is a year or two older. But you're forgetting I'm pretty mature for my age."

"You're right. Somehow that's an easy thing to forget."

Donny's grin faded. "Listen, Marie. You're meddling. Do I mix in with your boyfriends?"

"All the time!"

Impatiently, Donny thumped out a chord on the piano. "That's because *you* need guidance. Now, can we get back to the song?"

Out in the lobby, Mickey and J. L. were getting back to their own kind of work—finding the Osmonds. "Okay. So we know they're staying here," said Mickey. "But *where* here? How'll we find out?"

J. L. grinned. "Simple. See that delivery boy carrying flowers?"

"Yeah. So?"

"Well, he's going to *deliver* them, isn't he? You wait and watch." He crossed over to the boy. "Who are these flowers for, son?"

The boy checked the card. "Mrs. Otto von Kleinschmidt."

J. L. smiled. "Then they're for my wife. I'll take them."

Before the flower messenger could think it over, J. L. handed him a generous tip, helped himself to the bouquet and marched back to Mickey. "See? Easy. Now we just go over to the desk clerk and ask for the Osmonds' room number."

Mickey frowned. "We don't look like florist's boys, J. L. We'll never get away with it."

"Follow me! You gotta use your head, Mickey."

The pair went up to the desk. "I have some flowers for the Osmonds," J. L. said politely.

The clerk nodded and rang for a bellhop. "Suite one-o-eight," he said.

"They're in the rehearsal hall. Want me to take them there?" the bellhop asked.

"No. Suite one-o-eight."

Off went the bellhop and off went Mickey and J. L. "See? Easy," J. L. said. "Now all we gotta do is take a look around one-o-eight."

"Nope. *I* take a look around. You keep a lookout." Mickey chuckled. "As you say, J. L., you gotta use your head."

It was going to be better advice than even Mickey had thought!

Strains of music drifting along the corridor drew J. L. straight to the rehearsal hall. He peered in. His eyes widened. Mickey's room-search was going to wind up zero. J. L. hardly saw Marie. His gaze fastened on the object of the search. The necklace!

At the piano, Donny managed to keep an eye on his music and Tricia, too—an optical feat Marie noticed at once. Singing merrily, she edged her way between her brother and the object of his most sparkling smiles.

Almost as he struck the last note, Donny jumped up. "Not bad," he said cheerfully. "Why don't you go back to the room and grab a little rest?"

"Oh? What're you going to do?"

Donny shrugged. "Oh—I don't know. I kind of thought I'd walk around and see some of the sights."

Marie nodded. "Sights?" She glanced briefly at Tricia. "Good description."

"Look, Marie! She's a fan and for us to be a success we've got to be nice to fans. You know that. So you see—I'm doing this just for you."

"I can imagine. What I can't do is *believe.*"

"Aw, Marie. Come on! I'll be along in a few minutes."

Marie grinned. "Few minutes? Give you five, then I'm coming to look for you."

Quickly, J. L. ducked out into the corridor as Marie headed for the door. And quietly he followed along to Suite 108.

In the rehearsal hall Donny shuffled his music together. Tricia rose. "Hey! Where you going?" he called.

"I haven't finished unpacking," Tricia answered.

"Can't it wait? I thought maybe as we're both new here we might take a tour of the place."

"What about your sister?" Tricia asked.

"Oh, her. The trip's knocked her out. She's going to rest."

Tricia smiled sweetly. "I think I'll do the same." She started toward the door.

Donny rushed after her. "Uh . . . What room are you in?" he asked.

"One-nineteen," Tricia replied.

"I'm going that way. I'll walk you home."

As they slowly ambled to the door, Marie was stepping into Suite 108. She stared in disbelief. The room was a shambles! Clothes flung about, every piece of furniture dragged out of place, and even pictures hanging on a tilt. "Oh, no!" She took a backward step.

Swiftly a hand shot out and the door behind her slammed shut. She whirled around.

"I'm not going to hurt you," the intruder snarled. "Just hand me that—"

At the door of 119, Donny still hadn't given up hope. "Maybe we could go out later?"

"That'd be nice," Tricia agreed. "The three of us could do something."

"Sure. We could drive up to Diamond Head and—" He suddenly stopped. "The *three* of us?"

Tricia nodded. "You and me and Marie."

Donny swallowed. "Well . . . uh . . . y'see, Marie can't stay out too late. She's just a kid and she needs *a lot* of sleep."

"Oh, we could be back by nine—easily." Tricia's eyes twinkled. "Ten at the latest."

Donny sighed. "She'd never make it. At home

we call her 'Six O'Clock Osmond.' For her, Walter Cronkite is *The Late Show*." He sighed even more heavily. "Yeah. I guess we're just forced to go without her."

"I'm sure she'd hate to miss seeing Diamond Head."

"Don't you worry, Tricia. I'll tell her all about it." He beamed. "Call you about eight."

With that good feeling of things going right, Donny strode along the corridor, idly counting room numbers as he went. "One-seventeen. One-fifteen. Hmm. No one-thirteen. This hotel isn't taking any chances on bad luck!"

Neither was J. L. He'd deserted his listening post outside 108 the second Donny and Tricia had appeared.

Donny took up his count again. "One-eleven—"

A piercing scream cut the air. Donny would know that voice anywhere! ONE-O-EIGHT! He broke into a gallop. "Marie! I'm coming!" he shouted.

Inside the room, Mickey froze at the sound of Donny's voice. He eyed the door leading to the hotel balcony veranda and sped toward it just as Donny, crashing and sprawling, burst into the room. "You all right?" he asked anxiously.

Marie, hand at her throat, could only nod.

"Call Sid. I'm going after that guy!"

CHAPTER 4

~~~~~~

MICKEY WAS FAST. So was Donny. The Royal Hawaiian was left far behind them in the first three minutes of the chase, and Donny was gaining on Mickey with every reaching stride of his long legs.

Nearly winded, Mickey zipped around a corner and nipped into a doorway. Panting, and grim-faced, he took his usual standard running equipment out of his pocket—brass knuckles. He fitted them over his fist.

Unluckily for Mickey and *very* luckily for all who'd bought tickets for the Royal Hawaiian guest stars' performance, Donny was collecting a horde of speedy kids. Wildly screaming for autographs, they came on like a thundering herd.

Mickey gulped. "I can't fight an army. Where *was* that J. L. anyhow?" Not lingering a second longer, he pounded off. And Donny, autograph books waving under his nose, gave up, too. True to his fans, he signed—*and* signed.

In the hotel Sid paced the floor of 108. "So Donny broke in. And then what happened?"

"The crook took off and Donny went chasing after him," Marie replied.

Sid was stunned. "*Donny* went after the crook! Little skinny Donny? What's he going to do if he catches him? Sing?" He groaned. "Marie, do you realize by tonight you could be doing a single?"

"Sid!" Marie's great, dark eyes rounded in horror. "Don't *talk* that way. *Do* something. Get the police!"

Donny saved his sister and his business manager from going into shock by rushing in. "You okay, Marie?"

Sid didn't wait for Marie to even nod her head. He almost flung himself on Donny. "She's fine. What about you? You all right? No broken bones? Lemme see your teeth!"

"Sid, will you stop it! I'm fine."

But the Osmonds' business manager snatched Donny's jaw. "Thank goodness! If anything hap-

pened to those, we'd have to work three years
just to pay the orthodontist."

Donny sighed. "And for a second there, I
thought you were worrying about *me*." He
turned to Marie. "Anything missing?"

Marie shook her head. "Nothing. He didn't
take any jewelry or anything."

"Then what *was* he after?"

"I think—"

Sid interrupted. "John Denver! That's who it
was! He was after Donny's music. I never be-
lieved that sweetness-and-light stuff. You show
me a wholesome, clean-living person and I'll
show you—" He suddenly stopped, looked at his
two wholesome, clean-living stars, and looked
silly.

"What'll you show us, Sid?" Donny asked.

Sid looked even sillier. "Maybe it was Pat
Boone?"

"I think it was a plain thief after this necklace," Marie said.

Donny haw-hawed. "That piece of junk? No
way."

"I don't care *what* he was after," said Sid.
"I'm not taking any chances. I'm getting a private detective on you two."

"Look, Sid," Donny said pleadingly. "Nothing
was taken. It was probably some fan looking for
a souvenir. We don't need anyone looking over

our shoulders. Besides, I'm taking Marie to
Diamond Head tonight."

"Diamond Head!" Marie exclaimed. "My
goodness! We certainly *don't* need a private
detective, Sid."

Sid shook his head. "My decision is final.
You're both gonna be watched day and night."

Donny slammed his hands to his forehead.
"Sid!"

"Final," Sid repeated. "What would your
parents think, *plus* Jay and Merrill and Wayne
and Alan and Virgil and Tom and Jimmy and—"

"We know," Marie said gloomily. "And Uncle
Bruce and Aunt Ida. Right?"

"Right," Sid replied firmly.

About the same time Donny Osmond had expected to be viewing the tropical night from
Diamond Head, Mr. Wong's magnificent limousine rolled to a stop at the Royal Hawaiian.

Mr. Wong daintily set his small feet on the
pavement as Mickey and J. L. came up. "You've
been clumsy," he told his two employees. Very
clumsy. Obviously, I shall have to supervise
personally. Where are the two little darlings this
moment?"

"Inside," J. L. said gloomily. "They're going on
a TV show. It's a guest shot."

Mr. Wong smiled faintly. "Guest *shot?* How
appropriate!"

Mickey moved uneasily. "And what's-'er-name—she's *wearing* the necklace."

Mr. Wong lifted a delicate finger and tapped his chin. "You're positive Professor Kruse knows nothing about this?"

J. L. grinned. "Webster won't be talking to the Professor or anyone else. You can be sure of that."

J. L. was right. Webster wasn't talking. Except for one eye and the toes of one foot he was bandaged almost like an Egyptian mummy. With fear in his heart he listened to Professor Kruse who stood by the hospital bed.

Almost nobody looked at or listened to Professor Kruse without getting a heart full of fear. Grim, evil, icy, he was even more frightening than his henchman, Ito. More than one person had trembled in fright when the Professor lifted, in anger, his terrible, black-gloved, iron hand.

He leaned over the hospital bed. "How could you do this to me, Webster?" he grated out. "Years, *year*s of the most careful planning. All for nothing!"

The very thought of so much *nothing*, sent him into a frenzy. His artificial hand smashed down on the bedside table, and splinters went flying. The faithful Ito rushed forward to tidy up the mess. Webster trembled inside his bandages.

"We *must* know where that necklace is," Professor Kruse said sternly. "Be cooperative." He looked over at Ito. "Was there anything on him? Anything?"

"Only these torn pictures," Ito replied, holding out the tattered photographs of Donny and Marie.

For the next few minutes the interview went badly. Ito had no more information to give and Webster couldn't give what information he had.

The Professor shook his head in disgust. He was not one to settle for zero information. He stared icily at the helpless driver of the Okay Driving School learner's car. "Webster!" he bellowed. "I command you! Wiggle your toes."

Webster managed to make his big toe bob back and forth as though in friendly, obedient greeting. The Professor nodded slightly in return. "We have ways of making you talk." His voice lowered, keeping his gaze steadily on his employee's toe, he spoke again. "Now then—good! I shall ask you certain questions. Wiggle once for 'yes,' twice for 'no.' Understood?"

The toe nodded politely.

"The necklace," said Kruse. "Is it in Hawaii?" The toe replied with a single nod.

"I see," said the Professor. "Very good. Does a man have it?"

Two nods. The Professor frowned. For a moment, he paced the room and almost absentmindedly turned the knob on the TV set. A picture fluttered up on the screen. Professor Kruse recognized the *lanai* of the Royal Hawaiian, but there was no sound from the TV to interrupt his thinking. He paused and looked again at Webster's toe. "You say 'no,' then it must be a woman. Yes?"

The toe nodded agreement.

"Is she here alone?"

Two nods.

"Ah! Then perhaps a couple—a man and a woman? Hmm . . . who could it be."

As though it, too, was under the spell of Professor Kruse's overpowering personality, the TV blatted forth a sudden reply—"DONNY AND MARIE OSMOND! And they'll be with us in a minute," said the announcer.

At the hotel Sid made good use of that minute by having a quick conversation with the two stars. Behind the drapes that hid them from the audience he introduced the big man at his side. "Al Harris, kids. Al's going to look after you two."

Al grinned good-naturedly. "I'll be right over there when you get off the stage," he said. "Don't you worry."

Donny's eyes followed the big fellow as he walked away. "He doesn't look like a private detective. Are you sure he is, Sid?"

"Well, he's just starting out. He's an ex-con gone straight. Knows all the angles—inside and out. He's just perfect for the job."

Marie touched her necklace. "But—" she began.

There was no time to say more. The TV host's voice rang out—"And here they are. Donny and Marie Osmond!"

In the hospital room Professor Kruse, his back to the TV screen, scowled. "I can't think with that music going on. Ito, turn it off."

All of Webster's toes sprang into action. Up, down. Up, down. "Wait, Ito! A message is coming through! You want the TV to stay on?"

The toes bowed a single time.

"This is no time for enjoying TV, Webster," Professor Kruse said coldly. He turned to the screen in time to catch a view of a pleased audience. Mr. Wong, with J. L., sat square in the middle of the screen. "Wong!" the Professor gasped. "Ito, leave that knob alone. Wait."

The camera closed in on Marie, but Professor Kruse scarcely noticed the sparkling-eyed, pretty Miss Osmond. "The necklace!" he exclaimed. "There it is! Yes. Yes! Those people. Who are they?"

He rushed back to the bed and picked up the autographed picture. "Ah! the Osmonds. *Charley planted the necklace on that 'Marie' person!*"

Webster was so pleased that he had trouble keeping his toes from saying 'no' instead of 'yes.' He managed to stick with just one wiggle.

"Good work, Webster!" the Professor said in

his pleasantest voice. He checked his Lüger pistol and smiled faintly. "Now hurry up and get your strength back."

In his cordial way he swatted Webster encouragingly with his iron hand. "Get a good night's sleep."

It looked as though Webster couldn't wait. As the Professor and Ito left, even his toes had taken on a terribly sleepy look. The Professor's pats could put anything to sleep!

CHAPTER 5

~~~~~~~~~~~~~~~~~~~~~~~~

DONNY AND MARIE knew they had their audience with them. And, as always, that was magic. Both swung into the finale with extra enthusiasm and Marie even began sorting out special fans to sing to.

Suddenly, her voice scooted around a note instead of landing on it pure and true. "That face!" Quickly, she recovered and went on through the last of the lyric, managing not to glance at the unbelievably evil eyes that had glared into hers.

Outside the hotel Ito and Professor Kruse swirled up in a gleaming sports car. Together, they almost ran inside. Too late. At least too late to hear the Osmonds. "But not too late to *see* them," Professor Kruse muttered to Ito.

In Suite 108, Marie flung herself into a chair. "Where exactly are we going tonight, Donny?"

Donny became very interested in his shoelace. "Uh, well—I didn't know whether you'd be too tired . . . so . . . I sort of . . ." his voice trailed off.

Marie looked at him sharply. "So you *sort of* made a date with Grandma Tricia Moses?" She jumped up, went to the mirror and took off the necklace. "Don't explain. Hey! It's all *right!* It doesn't really matter. You two go find some great Hawaiian restaurant and dine under the stars. And don't worry one little bit about me. I can have a big night with Sid. You know him— he might even rent a car and take me out for a Big Mac."

"Aw, Marie!" Donny looked miserable.

His sister laughed. "Hey! I mean it. It doesn't matter. I enjoy Sid and I *do* want you to have a good time."

She started across the room, but Donny stopped her, his face and voice serious. "Marie, there's something I want to ask you."

Marie giggled. "You and Tricia can't decide on your silver pattern?"

"Be *serious*. Look, Marie," Donny tapped his chest. "Me—brother. You—sister. Right?"

Marie was in no mood to get deeply interested in the topic. "Sure," she laughed. "At least that's what Mom always said. And I've never been able to shake her on the story."

But Donny didn't laugh. "I'm older. You're younger. I'm smarter. You're dumb—"

"Hold it!" Marie's face changed. "You can settle for just 'older.' So I flubbed the song tonight. I know that. Now what's bothering you? I've already told you—a horrible, evil-looking man was staring at me *and* the necklace. It—it was just *awful*." She shuddered.

Donny groaned. "The necklace! That dumb necklace. *That's* what I want to talk about."

"So do I," Marie said quickly. "There's something very strange going on. First, that man broke in. Then—"

Donny sighed. "You've said that before. What makes you think he was after the necklace?"

Marie hesitated. "Oh, call it a crazy hunch. You see, when he came stalking after me, and being so threatening, a little voice deep inside, said, 'Marie—that person grabbing at your throat just *may* not be after your autograph.'"

Donny shrugged. "Right. He could have been after clothes . . . money."

Marie didn't seem to hear him. She looked at the necklace in her hand. "There must be something special about this."

"Special!" Donny laughed. "That? Hey, I bet it's the mysterious jeweled eye of an idol . . .

stolen from a temple by a white hunter who must get it back or be cursed forever." He opened his eyes wide and faked a horrified expression. "Marie—come *on!*"

But Marie shook her head. "No, really. It might be valuable! She picked up a shiny metal box from the coffee table and lifted the cover. "I found this little box and it's just right for the necklace. I'll just put it in here."

Donny watched her pluck up a cleaning tissue and begin shining the cover. He frowned. "Sis, your imagination is running away with you. And its affecting your work . . . your career. Please, Marie—that necklace is only a piece of glass. Throw it away!"

"I couldn't, Donny. After all, the little priest said the orphans saved their pennies to buy it for me."

Donny sighed. "He sure did. And you don't think orphans' pennies bought some kind of rare jewel, do you? It's getting on your nerves. Marie —I'm your older brother. I always know what's best. Dump it!"

"You always know what's best! Well, that's news!" Angrily, Marie popped the cover into place, put down the box, and flounced off to her bedroom.

Just as angrily, Donny bent over the coffee table. He glared at the metal box. "You *trouble*-maker, you!" he stormed.

Pressed back behind window draperies in the corridor Tricia peered carefully and watched Donny go striding by her hiding place. As he turned into a side corridor, she stepped out, taking an automatic pistol from her handbag. Swiftly, she walked toward Suite 108. The elevator doors opposite the Osmond suite slid open. Out stepped Mr. Wong, Mickey, and J. L.

Coolly, Tricia eased the automatic back into her handbag and kept right on walking with never a backward look.

Behind her, the group stopped at the door next to 108. Mr. Wong produced a room key. "Now this room has a handy connecting balcony. You know what to do."

J. L. looked uneasy. "What about the Professor? I'm sure I saw him across the lobby."

"Yeah," Mickey agreed. "And he had that dumb Oriental with him." He failed to notice Mr. Wong's suddenly icy stare. And, to make his point clearer, he pushed up the corners of his eyes, "Y'know the one who—"

Suddenly he felt Mr. Wong's stinging look. He speedily pretended to be rubbing tired eyes. "Er—" he said weakly, "the one who's a very snappy dresser."

"We shall get the necklace well ahead of the Professor's attempt," Mr. Wong said coldly. "Won't we, Mickey?"

* * *

Professor Kruse and Ito stepped out from the same elevator that had carried Mr. Wong, J. L., and Mickey up from the lobby. Tricia, walking back again, spotted them just as Professor Kruse turned the key in the door next to 108. She went quietly past them, hesitated at her own door, then stepped inside.

Marie, in her bedroom, pushed hangers along the closet rack. Carefully, she looked at each dress. She lifted out a pale yellow, floaty silky one, decided it wouldn't go with a Big Mac, and put it back. From the living room came the sound of a door opening softly. "Donny?" she called out.

No reply. "Sid?" she called out again.

Suddenly a chilly feeling crept along her arms. *Maybe that awful man's come back. . . . Nonsense! Sid had hired that big Al Harris to keep them safe.* Briskly she went to the living room door and swung it open. Darkness!

A big Hawaiian moon, silvery palm fronds, and the sweet fragrance of ginger blossoms wafting in from the open balcony doors were wasted on Marie. She wished Donny had turned on at least one lamp before going into his bedroom. "Hey, Donny! You're conserving too much energy," she called, as she crossed over to his doorway.

She began to reach for the knob—and froze! Moonlight glimmered on its metal surface as it slowly *turned.* She gasped in horror and stepped back, still staring at it. Now the knob wasn't turning at all. "Just this funny moonlight!" She gulped, and turned away feeling half-ashamed of her galloping imagination and half-doubting it *was* all imagination.

If she had looked just then toward the billowing draperies at the balcony doors, she would have flown straight out into the corridor. Her doubts would have been settled. Mr. Wong's eyes watched her every move!

But Marie's spirits were rising. The room didn't seem half as dark as it seemed when she'd first walked in. She could even see the little metal box gleaming on the coffee table. Then from a closet door came a dull *thud*. She jumped, eyed the door, and made up her mind. *I'll investigate. If I don't, I'll just scare myself to death wondering*.

Bravely, she walked over, and biting her lips for courage, flung it open. A dark shape slid forward. But before a scream could rise in her throat, the dark shape became a suitcase, falling forward from the packed closet.

She giggled shakily. "So you're the intruder! Never depend on Donny to pack away the luggage!"

But in spite of this comforting thought, Marie fled back to the even more comforting electric lights in her bedroom. She settled herself at her dressing table and picked up a hand-mirror, and for the third time in only minutes, her heart jumped in fear. Reflected in the mirror was the cruelest face she had ever seen! She whirled around. Nothing! Nobody!

Professor Kruse could move fast when he wanted to!

Almost as she decided Hawaii was having some strange effect upon her usual perky self, she once again heard a door in the living room close softly. And before she could begin to really shake apart, she sped back to that frightening place. But this time, she went straight to a desk lamp and turned it on. Nobody! And in the glow of lamplight, the room was not in the least frightening. She turned back to her bedroom, paused by the coffee table, and stared down. The cover of the little metal box was tilted on its side. Without touching it Marie knew what she'd find —or *not* find! And suddenly the room seemed awful again. In a burst of fright she rushed over and flung open the corridor door.

This time a scream really did crowd up in her throat. A figure wearing a hideous *tiki* mask loomed in the entrance.

"How do you like it?" a familiar voice asked. "The old Hawaiian god of something-or-other. Be a nice prop for the show. Hey, Marie! What's the matter?"

"Sid!" her voice trembled. "My necklace! It's gone!"

CHAPTER 6

~~~~~~~~~~~~~~~~~~~~~~~~~~~~~~~~~~~~

GUESTS IN THE Royal Hawaiian never had reason to see the dimly-lit, cavernous service tunnels filled with the equipment that made their vacation comfortable.

But it was an ideal place for a thief to catch a thief. And Professor Kruse backed into the shadows, holding his Lüger steady, and watched Mr. Wong's Mickey come warily down the stairs.

Mickey, too, was well armed. Holding his .38 tightly, he went pussyfooting past the Professor. *Just* past. A sudden jab in the back brought him to a sudden halt. He speedily dropped his .38.

"Leaving so soon?" the Professor asked. "How very impolite." He kicked Mickey's gun into the shadows and circled in front of him. "Put it there," he demanded, "there on top of that box." He motioned to a big wooden packing crate.

"I haven't got it," Mickey edged back.

"Don't move!" the Professor warned. "Read that sign!"

Mickey looked up toward a maze of electrical wiring. DANGER 32,000 VOLTS. He almost turned into a statue.

"So . . . the necklace, if you please." Professor Kruse grinned mirthlessly.

Mickey started to speak, looked past the Professor, and sighed in relief. "Mr. Wong is just behind you," he said, confidence back in his voice.

"Please." The Professor looked bored. "That one's been used so often! So amateurish! Just step back."

Mr. Wong spoke. "That won't be necessary, Mickey."

It was the Professor's turn to freeze, and Mr. Wong stepped around, helped himself to the Professor's Lüger, and sent it skidding along the floor. "Now," he said, "the necklace mentioned. Place it on that box."

The Professor stared hard at Mr. Wong, then turned to Mickey. "I fear the 'honorable' Mr. Wong is not at all honorable. *He* has it."

"Quickly, Professor!" Mr. Wong said. "Put it on the box."

Professor Kruse smiled. "Mr. Wong—if you care to look behind you, you will discover *my* associate, with, I fear, a drawn revolver."

Mr. Wong merely uttered a soft "tsk tsk!" "I fear you must do better than that, Professor. Now hand it over."

Ito's voice grated behind him. "That won't be necessary!"

"Oh, but it will be, Professor," Mr. Wong said softly. "I might mention an associate of *mine* is behind your Mr. Ito."

The Professor sighed. "Come, come. We've had quite enough of that. I believe a search of your person is necessary. Please remove your jacket."

"*That* won't be necessary," said J. L., behind Ito. .

Mr. Wong smiled. "You mentioned a personal search. . . . If you will remove *your* jacket . . ."

The Professor stared at Mr. Wong. Mr. Wong stared back.

"Ah!" Mr. Wong sighed. "I believe you may be thinking as I am. Yes?"

Kruse nodded.

"That a *third* force is at work against the two of us?"

The Professor nodded again. "It would appear to be in our mutual interest to . . . er . . . team up?"

Donny and Marie in the wreckage of their motor-bike—the aftermath of a high-speed chase and crash along the road up Honolulu's Mount Tantalus.

Marie does battle with Mickey (Ted Cassidy) as he tries to steal the mysterious necklace.

The Bad Guys, from left, Professor Kruse (Kenneth Mars), Mr. Wong (Khigh Deigh), Mickey (Ted Cassidy), Jake (Charles Walker), and Ito (Harold Sakata), are stopped in mid-pursuit.

Khigh Deigh (left) and Kenneth Mars, who play Mr. Wong and the wacky Professor Kruse, turn a flaming tropical punch into a mini-bonfire during Donny and Marie's nightclub act.

Donny and Marie's much-harried manager, Sid (Herb Edelman), finally goes overboard during the sea-chase segment. Mr. Wong (Khigh Deigh, on right) scowls at the scene.

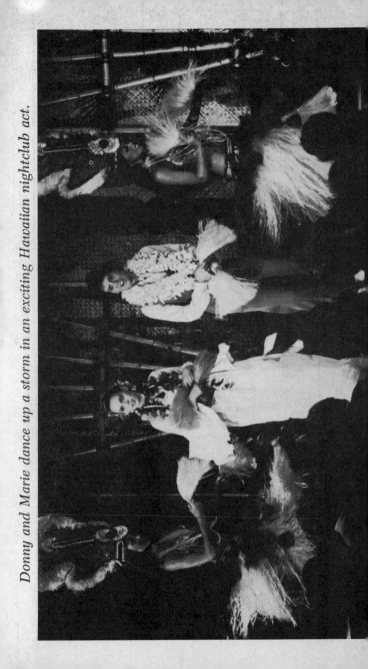

Donny and Marie dance up a storm in an exciting Hawaiian nightclub act.

Mr. Wong rubbed his chin and looked thoughtful.

"Hey! What's going on here?" Mickey asked.

Mr. Wong sighed. "You have not thought of it, Mickey? *None* of us has the necklace. It was taken by a third party whom we must seek out."

"And *destroy!*" exclaimed Professor Kruse, slamming his iron hand down on the packing crate. Splinters flew. The iron hand jammed. The Professor didn't seem to notice. "But who? *Who?* Who did it?"

There was no reply as the faithful Ito set to work freeing his employer's deadly hand from the splintered crate.

Mr. Wong cleared his throat. "If that is agreed, I suggest an immediate search for the weapons so generously scattered in this disagreeable tunnel."

After a thorough search, all guns were once again with their owners. All, that is, but Professor Kruse's Lüger. Not since the age of two had tears nearly welled up in those icy eyes. "My Lüger!" he wailed. "Has *nobody* seen my Lüger?"

While the Professor was being desperately unhappy in the hotel service tunnel, Donny was not too happy in the hotel lobby. With Sid, he strolled up to the Make-a-Wish fish pond. Coins gleamed below in patches between clusters of lily pads.

"I did it for her own good," he said stubbornly. "Sid, *relax!*"

"For her own *good!*" Sid sputtered. "You stole her necklace! You're the *thief!* When this gets out, you got any idea what it'll do to the sale of the Donny Osmond Cuddly Doll?"

Donny pulled the stolen property from his pocket and instantly, Sid's hand reached out to cover it with his hand. "Careful! Someone might be looking!" he exclaimed.

"Sid, *you* look. It's just a dumb piece of glass. But Marie's just seeing gangsters everywhere. And you heard her flub the song!"

"But Donny . . ."

"Don't worry. It'll all be okay. She'll be her own sweet self again without that necklace on her mind all the time. Are you going upstairs now? I have to find Tricia."

Sid nodded. Donny suddenly dropped the necklace in the pond. A goldfish sashayed by— lily pads stirred, and the necklace disappeared from sight. "I bet Marie's forgotten it already," Donny grinned. "Let's go."

Sid didn't look so sure. He gazed at the pond a second, then turned to catch up with Donny.

Donny wasn't so sure, either, when the two stepped off the elevator. A policeman stood outside Room 108. Recognizing Donny, he opened the door, and a puzzled Sid and Donny stepped into the living room.

Marie's dark eyes were flashing as she excitedly paced the room. "Lieutenant Alecki, this is a terrible, terrible thing. Whoever took it should be *caught* and *arrested* and sent to *jail*."

Sid paled as the Lieutenant nodded and said, "We'll certainly do the best we can."

Marie turned and saw her brother with Sid. "Oh, Donny! Did you know my necklace was stolen?"

Sid answered quickly, "He knew."

Donny's voice was soothing, but his words weren't. "Look, it's really not at all that important. It's just a piece of glass. I'm sure the police have better things—"

"It *is* important. There's a *principle* involved," his sister said fiercely.

"Marie—maybe it's all for the best. And, after all, there's nothing we can do about it."

To his dismay Lieutenant Alecki held up a small, transparent plastic bag. Inside was the metal box. "There *is* something we can do about it. Whoever it was, he left a beautiful set of fingerprints."

Donny forced a smile so frozen he could barely shape his next word. "Fingerprints?"

"Remember?" Marie said eagerly. "I wiped the box clean after I put the necklace in. Wasn't that lucky?"

Donny tried to look as though Marie was very clever, and Lieutenant Alecki stood up and started for the door. "I'll get this right over to the lab for photographs. They'll be run through the computer. Could have an answer for you real soon."

The door closed behind him and Marie struck her hands together. "Oh, we'll catch him. I just know we'll catch him!"

Almost right away there was a knock at the door. Sid went forward. "For your sake," he muttered to Donny, "I hope it's some famous criminal lawyer. You're going to need one."

Alas! It was only Tricia. "Hi. I heard about the necklace. I'm *really* sorry," she said.

"Yeah," Donny said. "Bad luck. Well, if you girls will excuse me—I'll be right back."

"Me, too," Sid added.

Once again, the two started for the lobby fish pond. Donny stopped at a bench and Sid watched him tug off shoes and socks, and roll up pant legs.

Walking wearily to the pond, a tourist couple came. "We just have to end this wonderful day by making a wish, dear," said the lady.

"Yes," her tired husband sighed. "Let's wish for a good night's sleep." He took a coin from his pocket and tossed it in. The two began to stroll away. Circles still rippled in the pond as the barefoot Donny walked up. The couple turned and watched as he stepped into the pond and began groping between ripples and lily pads.

Looking pleased, he straightened, and waded out of the pond. Fast as possible he walked back to the bench with Sid.

"That *was* him, wasn't it?" the man asked his wife.

She nodded. "Donny Osmond. Harry . . .?"

"Yeah?"

"How much did you throw in?"

"A nickel."

They both thought that over. "I guess their albums aren't selling," he said.

"Sad," said she. They went on their way, both shaking their heads.

J. L., Ito, Mickey, and Mr. Wong sat nervously waiting in Mr. Wong's beautifully furnished library for Professor Kruse to wind up his telephone call.

"Good . . . good . . . good," they heard him say.

He hung up. "That was my contact at the crime lab. When they have the name to go with the fingerprints, we shall be the first to know."

"Excellent," said Mr. Wong. "How fortunate to learn the police are already on the trail."

"But," said the Professor quickly, "*we* shall

learn the news almost before they do. And *when* we do, we shall *strike him down.*"

He raised his deadly, iron hand over a delicate vase ready to smash it to smithereens. Like a cat, Mr. Wong leaped up and whisked his treasure to safety.

"Oh, sorry, Wong," the Professor murmured. "I just felt like striking down *something.*"

"I understand," said Mr. Wong politely.

Donny, once more properly dressed in shoes and socks, rose from the lobby bench. "Let's go, Sid."

Sid's worried frown deepened. "You mean you're just going to go back up there, walk in, and tell her you *took* it? She'll kill you!"

Donny looked gloomy. "There's no other way. I'll just try to explain . . ."

Al Harris, the newly hired private eye came walking up. "Excuse me, but the car's ready whenever you are."

Donny thanked him and watched him walk away through the lobby. "Sid," he said suddenly. "Maybe there *is* another way. Al could put it back."

"Al!"

"*He* used to be a burglar. Right? He could break in . . . return the necklace and leave a nice note saying he was sorry he did it. Then

Marie would drop charges, call off the police. It'd be perfect."

Without waiting for Sid's opinion, Donny rushed off and caught up with the ex-burglar. "Al! Al, I want to ask for a favor."

"You got it, Mr. Osmond," Al smiled warmly.

"Donny."

"Okay—Donny. Be happy to do anything at *all*. I'm so grateful to you for giving me this chance to go straight. What is it?"

Donny's voice dropped low. "I want you to break into a room."

Al stared, thunderstruck. "You want me to break into a room?" he asked slowly.

Donny nodded.

Al stared a moment, then grinned widely. "I get it. You're *testing* me."

Donny shook his head. "No. I mean it." He glanced quickly around, leaned close to Al and whispered, "Tonight!"

Al's grin faded. "What are you after?"

"Nothing," said Donny.

"Nothing?"

"I mean—I don't want to take anything *out*." He held out the necklace. "I want you to put this *in*."

Al stared at the necklace and then stared harder at Donny. "Look, Mr. Osmond," he said slowly, "That's not exactly the way it works. I don't want to seem like a know-it-all, but in the

burglary game, you take *out*, not put *in*." He
hesitated. "Now, whose room you planning to
break in?"

"Mine."

Al's mouth popped open. He shook his head.
"Can I say something? Stick with the singing."
He put his hand over the necklace. "Forget all
this. Because I can promise you—going at it the
way you are, crime definitely will *not* pay."

"No, no, Al. Listen." He took Al's arm. "I'd
better explain. Here, let's walk over to that
desk. I'll tell you all about it and then—well,
you'll understand."

Al didn't understand at all. But he was not
the sort of man to break a promise. He carefully
wrote as Donny dictated. ". . . and I only did it
for my poor starving wife and children." Donny
paused. "Make that *four* children, Al. Marie
loves kids."

Al mopped his forehead. "Boy, going straight
is more confusing than I thought. Putting a
necklace *in* a room! You sure the room will be
empty when I make the heist? I mean . . .
when I *don't* make the heist?"

Donny nodded. "I'll take Marie out with me.
You'll have plenty of time. You keep an eye
on our balcony door. When you see me signal,
that'll mean we're leaving. I'll go to the room
now. Watch for me and my signal."

Al folded the note and tucked it in a pocket

along with the necklace. He sighed heavily. "Okay. You can count on me."

Marie and Tricia stopped talking as Donny came bouncing into the living room of 108. Marie stood up. "Well, here he is, Tricia. Have fun, you two."

Donny laughed. "What's this 'you two' business? You're coming with us."

"You want me along?" Marie asked, puzzled.

Donny patted her shoulder. "You're my sister, aren't you?"

Marie nodded. "And I was also your sister an hour ago. But I wasn't invited then!"

"Oh, come on, Marie," Tricia said warmly. "It'll be fun and get your mind off things." She took Marie's arm and steered her toward the door.

In a flash, Donny zipped to the balcony door and whipped out a handkerchief. He gave it a brisk wave Al couldn't miss, then hurried to follow the girls. "Okay!" he exclaimed cheerfully. "The night is young! Let's go."

CHAPTER 7

IN THE LOBBY, Sid looked at the approaching threesome approvingly. "Glad to see you're getting out of that room, Marie," he said, walking over to them. "Where're you kids going?"

"We thought we'd find a luau," Donny replied. "We're all in the mood for a real Hawaiian feast."

"First we'd better find a cab," Marie suggested practically.

"Why a cab?" Sid asked. "Al will drive you—er, no, I just remembered—he's busy with something else. Oh, well—a cab's no problem. I'll get one for you. And Marie—you just go out and have a good time. Don't even think about the necklace."

Marie's hand flew to her forehead. "The necklace! What am I thinking about? Donny, you two go on. I have to be here when the police call about the fingerprints."

She began to hurry toward the elevators, and Donny, giving Sid one exasperated look, went rushing after her. Tricia shrugged. "Might as well make it a parade," she said, and marched after the two Osmonds.

Donny hoped they'd have a long wait for the elevator. But no. In seconds, they were whisked one flight up. Marie already had the room key out. Donny rushed past her. Nervously he thumped on the door of 108.

"Donny," Marie's voice was cool but not calming. "Got a minute for a question?" She waggled the room key. "Why are you knocking?"

Donny tried a lighthearted chuckle. "You know what Mom's always taught us, respect for other people's privacy." He loudly swatted the door again.

Gently, Marie brought his wrist down. "But *we're* the people, Donny. And we're not in there. We're out here. See? Turn around. Take a look." She grinned at Tricia. "He's got to start wearing a hat in the sun." Stepping to the door, she moved the key toward the lock.

"Allow me," Donny said swiftly—and just as swiftly dropped the key.

He bent to one knee and brushed his fingers across the carpeting. "Where could it have gone?" he asked in an amazed way. "Anybody see it?"

"You're kneeling on it," Marie replied. She looked over at Tricia. "Do you have brothers?"

Tricia laughed. "No. As a matter of fact, I don't. Why?"

Marie waved a hand toward Donny. "Would you like this one? He's had all his shots."

"And I'm good with *children*. Don't forget *that*, Marie," Donny said, getting to his feet.

"But not with keys, dear brother. Here. Better let me unlock this door. I'd like to be *inside* when the phone rings."

She swung the door open just in time to glimpse a man rush toward the balcony door, bump into a chair, and stumble forward.

"Stay back, girls!" Donny yelled. "He may be dangerous. I'll handle this!"

As neither Marie nor Tricia had moved an inch forward, Donny's grip on their arms seemed slightly unnecessary. And as Donny hadn't moved an inch forward, either, Al was the only one who didn't think Donny's action downright *peculiar*. He leaped up and aimed once more for the balcony.

Tricia bolted away from Donny. WHAM!

No sooner was Al's foot on the balcony than she expertly back-flipped him straight to the middle of the living room floor. Dazed, the big man stared up at them. "*Al!*" Marie gasped. "It's *Al!*"

Donny stood motionless and open-mouthed, staring at the totally unexpected wonder woman Tricia had turned out to be.

"Donny," Marie repeated. "I said it's *Al!*"

Donny's voice came over weakly. "He probably just came up to see if we needed any protection."

"Oh, Al," Marie groaned. "How could you do. . . "

"Wait a minute!" Al panted. He sat up. "Wait! I can explain. Y'see—"

Donny whipped out his handkerchief and brought it across Al's mouth.

"Donny! What are you doing!" Marie exclaimed.

"You always gag prisoners," Donny answered wildly. "It's part of their rights."

Tricia, not a hair out of place in spite of her recent highly acrobatic stunt, looked coolly past the excited threesome. "Everything in the room seems to be in order," she said. "We must have scared him off just in . . . Look! The necklace!" She hurried to the table and picked it up.

Donny beamed happily. "Then he was *returning* it! Read the note with it!"

Tricia glanced back to the table. "No note," she said.

Donny looked sharply at Al. "*No note?*" he asked loudly.

"Note?" Al blinked, then opened his jacket and reached for an inside pocket.

"Oh, there it is!" Donny cried. He snatched it out before Al's hand had even touched the "confession." "Here, Marie. You read it."

Marie unfolded the note. "*I am returning your necklace. The experience has taught me to give up a life of crime and I am grateful. Please forgive me. I was only doing it for my starving wife . . .*"

Marie's voice trembled. She looked up. "It's so sad—"

"Go on," Donny urged. "His starving wife and four children."

Marie glanced at the note again. "Why! You're right, Donny. How'd you know?"

Donny's face became a little pink. "Er, I happened to remember it from something that was said."

He reached for the note and handed it to Al. "Marie, Al did return your necklace. Let's give him a second chance."

Before Marie could reply, the phone rang. As she went over to answer it, Al turned to Tricia. "It was just for my little ones . . . my three little ones." He hastily checked the note.

"I mean *four*. They came so fast it's hard to keep up."

But Tricia's attention was on Marie's phone conversation. "Oh, yes, Lieutenant," she was saying.

"Miss Osmond," Lieutenant Alecki reported, "I just got the lab report. I'm sorry but there weren't any other fingerprints—just yours and your brother's."

"But there *had* to be!" Marie exclaimed. "You see we just—" She suddenly stopped speaking and glanced over at the others. Donny was succeeding in getting Tricia's attention and Al was busy rubbing an aching back. But Marie lowered her voice when she spoke to Lieutenant Alecki. "Just mine and *Donny's?* Oh, I see. Thank you, Lieutenant."

Blocking any view of the phone she first pressed down the receiver button, then spoke loudly. "You mean I can't drop charges?" she asked the now phantom lieutenant in a voice filled with dismay. "Oh. You say whoever's fingerprints are on the box will have to stand trial?"

Donny, listening, turned pale. Al quickly whispered to him. "Don't worry. I know everybody in the big house. I'll give you introductions."

But Donny was becoming even paler. "Marie —" he began.

His sister held up a halting hand. Again she

spoke into the dead phone. "You mean he'll get at least *five* years?"

Stunned, Donny repeated, "Five *years!*"

"Well," Marie spoke sadly, "if that's the law, I guess—"

"Marie!" Donny strode up and caught at her elbow. "Marie, I have a confession. Y'see—I was the one—"

The phone rang sharply. Donny stared down at Marie's finger on the receiver button, and Marie stared coldly at Donny. She released the button. "Hello? Yes, Sid. He called. Tell the taxi to wait. Hotfingers will be down in a minute."

She hung up. "Donny how could you do it? And *why?*"

Donny flushed red. "I meant well," he began stumblingly. "You were getting so bugged by that stupid necklace . . . and I thought if it was gone—"

Marie cut in. "If I was getting *that* bad, you should've just told me. I'd have thrown it away."

Donny sighed. "Then why don't you do it? Throw it away."

Marie looked at the necklace. "Nope! I'm *really* bugged by it now."

In Mr. Wong's house, Professor Kruse talked on the phone to his special connection at the crime lab. He was plainly annoyed. "There were no strange fingerprints? None at all? No clue as to who took it?" He snorted angrily. "Please inform your associates that there are taxpayers here who are entitled to more protection and better police work!"

He slammed down the phone. "Disgraceful! The only fingerprints found were those Osmonds'!"

"What now?" Mickey asked.

Mr. Wong frowned. "You know—these Osmonds, they may be more clever than we think."

Professor Kruse nodded. "Very good thinking, Wong. I've never bought that innocent little act I've heard that they do. Very goodygoody, I understand. 'Aren't you a nice brother . . . aren't you a nice sister.'"

Mr. Wong tapped his chin. "Now let us think. Only *their* fingerprints. Let us suppose they wanted to throw us off the track. What better way than to say they no longer have the necklace?"

"Can you imagine such dishonesty?!" the Professor exclaimed angrily.

Mr. Wong did not give an opinion. He continued, "I propose we keep a very watchful eye on those two."

"Excellent!" Professor Kruse agreed. "Tomorrow let us rendezvous at my office. There, we shall plan our attack!" He clapped his hands together with such force that a vase across the room toppled from its stand and smashed to bits.

Mr. Wong's evil eyes blazed. He leaped to his feet and pointed to his once beautiful vase. "The Osmonds!" he cried, voice trembling. "They shall pay for *that!* I, myself, shall revenge the loss of my treasured possession!"

Turning to the Professor, he bowed. "Until tomorrow then!"

CHAPTER 8

~~~~~~~~~~~~~~~~~~~~~~~~~~~~~~

TRYING TO KEEP a "very watchful eye" on the two Osmonds the next morning was bringing Mickey close to collapse. Mounted on a mule, he dutifully followed the pair and their tall, beautiful friend who'd been capering about on horseback viewing waterfalls. Without the help of Ito and J. L., he'd never have been able to last out the morning.

"Don't those kids ever have to rehearse?" he muttered. "They've seen a volcano, they've been waterskiing and surfing, and now it's horse-backing."

The mule twitched his ears. Otherwise, he had nothing to say. But relief was in sight for Mickey. Lunchtime. He hastily switched from muleback to taxi, followed the threesome, and waited until the three emerged from a restaurant.

Marie, not the least aware that her necklace was once again heading her for trouble, waved a hand toward a big open touring car and Al drove up to the restaurant curb. "You guys do the shopping tour," she said to Donny and Tricia. "I'm going back to the hotel and take it easy."

"Okay," Donny agreed. "But I wish you'd let that dumb necklace take it easy, too. I can't imagine why you'd want to wear it."

Marie smiled sweetly and stepped into the waiting car. "But for you, I just might throw it away."

"Marie!" Tricia gasped. "You mustn't!"

Donny's sister only grinned and waved back as Al pulled out. Tricia watched the big car roll smoothly into traffic. "She won't throw it away, will she?" she asked worriedly.

Donny shrugged. "I don't know. But I sure hope she does. Why?"

Tricia smiled very faintly. "Oh . . . it's so pretty. It would be a shame to just *dump* it."

Professor Kruse paced his spacious and quite handsome office waiting for Mr. Wong to get off the phone. What he heard Mr. Wong say made him pace faster.

"You lost her in traffic, you say? Ahh. But she *was* wearing the necklace. Good!"

The Professor paused long enough to do a happy dance step, but Mr. Wong's next words brought him to a raging halt.

"She what? Said she might *throw it away!* Mickey, return here immediately. All of you." Mr. Wong put down the phone. "You heard?" he asked the Professor.

"I heard," Professor Kruse said grimly. He raised his lethal iron hand and slammed it down on a frail piece of furniture.

To Mr. Wong's disappointment, it failed to shatter as *his* property had done the night before!

In front of the Royal Hawaiian, Marie stepped from the car just as Lieutenant Alecki came out from the hotel. "Oh, Lieutenant!" she called, hurrying up to him. "I'm so glad I ran into you. My necklace was recovered. See? It was all kind of my fault. I'm very sorry you were troubled."

The Lieutenant smiled. "I'm pleased you have it back. But if it's valuable perhaps you should put it in the hotel vault."

"That's just it," Marie said. "I don't know if it *is* valuable. Who could tell me?"

"Any good jeweler," Lieutenant Alecki replied. "It looks Hawaiian to me. You might try the museum. The director there, a Professor Kruse, is an expert on such things."

"Great idea! I'll just do that."

Saying good-bye to the Lieutenant, Marie turned back to the curb, but Al had already driven on his way. She hesitated, then, slinging her shoulderbag in place, she walked down the street to a motorcycle shop. In a matter of minutes she had a shiny motorbike to ride and clear instructions on the shortest way to reach the museum.

In the museum office, Professor Kruse sat forlornly at his desk. Not even the safe return of his lost Lüger seemed to have cheered him up. He looked from Mr. Wong to Mickey and J. L., then at his own man, Ito. "So now we know where the necklace is—around that Marie person's neck. *But where is the neck?* Where? I want that necklace. A fortune is slipping through our fingers!"

The "neck" was just outside his office door speaking with Miss Christie, the Professor's dependable secretary. And Miss Christie was very pleased to be meeting one of her favorite entertainers. In fact, she was so pleased that she broke a rule ideal secretaries never break—she buzzed his phone even though she knew he must be very busy with his callers.

"I know the name means nothing to you, Professor," she said excitedly, "but it does to me. It's Marie Osmond! She comes from this nice big family and she has this TV show with her brother. I just *love* them."

Professor Kruse forgot all about his trusty Lüger. Marie Osmond! He almost trembled as he got to his feet, hands clenched. "Excuse me, Mr. Wong, I must step outside a moment."

Miss Christie very nearly skipped off to meet him. "Forgive the good Professor, my dear," she said when her boss failed to even say 'howdy-do.' "He doesn't watch TV. He doesn't recognize you."

She turned to the frozen Professor. "This little dear has a necklace to be examined."

"How do you do, Professor Kruse," Marie said politely.

"Come over here to the light, my dear," Miss Christie said, leading Marie to a window.

Behind them Professor Kruse clenched his fists so hard that his iron hand tumbled to the floor. "Excuse me. Back in a moment," he said, picking up the hand.

It seemed to Mr. Wong that the Professor looked extremely happy for a man who was trying to fit an artificial hand back into position.

"Any calls?" the Professor asked, trying to keep joy from jumping out of his throat. "Any further information?"

Mr. Wong eyed the Professor sharply. He shook his head.

"Look," the gleeful art expert said, "I have

a little business outside. Not important. It will only take a minute. I will lock this door so you won't be disturbed." Flashing a phony smile, he departed.

"Disturbed by whom, I wonder?" Mr. Wong said softly. Gently he tried the doorknob. They were locked in all right!

To Miss Christie's great disappointment, the Professor gave her the rest of the day off. Sadly, she left the two at the window. The Professor took only one quick look at the necklace in Marie's hand. "I'm sorry. It is just a cheap souvenir, made here by the thousands during World War II. No value whatsoever."

"That's what my brother thought," Marie sighed. She started to drop the necklace in her shoulderbag.

"No, no, my dear!" said the Professor. "For so charming a visitor, allow me to replace it with something more suitable."

"No. I couldn't let you do that."

"*You must!*" cried Kruse. He recovered his calm. "I mean—it would be my pleasure. One moment."

Off he dashed to a room containing glass display cases. Too nervous to fit keys into locks, he smashed down his fist for faster action—unfortunately, his *real* fist.

And as he danced about in pain, Donny Osmond arrived at the museum. "Good thing the

Lieutenant knew where you went, Marie. Sid wants us right back for wardrobe fittings."

Into the office stepped Professor Kruse, handkerchief wrapped around his hand, and awkwardly holding out a new necklace.

"Oh, Professor," Marie said. "This is my brother, Donny."

"How do you do, sir," Donny nodded as the Professor was plainly in no shape to shake hands.

"He says it's el junko, Donny."

Professor Kruse smiled bravely. "But I would like to replace—"

"Thank you, Professor," Marie said hurriedly. "But junk or not, I've grown fond of it. It was given to me by such a sweet little—"

"Marie," Donny interrupted, feeling a long story about the little orphans was about to be told. "We must rush. Nice meeting you, sir." He escorted Marie out the door.

"Not so fast!" Kruse roared. He reached for his holster. No Lüger. Desperately, he made a dash for his own office only to discover a locked door. Now the necklace tangled in his key ring. Another delay before he burst into the room and sped to the Lüger on his desk. "Quick. Come! She's out there!" he cried.

"That was your 'nothing little business'?" asked Mr. Wong, eyes glinting dangerously.

But there was no time to lose. Teamwork was necessary. Out they all dashed, brandishing their weapons, only to come to a skidding stop. Lieutenant Alecki stood by his police car! Swiftly, each threw a gun into the shrubbery. Professor Kruse waved an innocent, friendly goodbye.

"Thanks for the lift, Lieutenant," said Donny, getting on the motorbike.

Marie waved to the group at the museum entrance and climbed on the bike. Off they zoomed, leaving a quarreling bunch of gun-toters searching for whose was whose among the bushes.

"This has gone far enough!" Mr. Wong cried. "Head them off! *Use* the guns!"

Riding along the curving road, the Osmonds were not in the least aware that life was about to become almost too exciting.

"Don't go so fast, Donny," Marie yelled. "I want to see the scenery."

Donny nodded and cut speed. He glimpsed a big car pulling up fast behind them. Oddly enough, it slowed as soon as it came even with them. Marie's arms suddenly clutched hard around his waist. "Speed it up! That driver! He's the burglar you chased."

One swift glance was all Donny needed. "Hang on!" he shouted.

Two shots cracked out above the zoom of the motorbike. Donny zigzagged expertly. Behind them, tires screeched on the sharply curving road. More shots. Once again Donny shouted, "HANG ON!"

For a second they were airborne as Donny skidded the bike in a sharp sweep off the highway and onto a narrow footpath. Bouncing wildly downhill, plumes of dust billowing, the Osmonds made the most spectacular exit from public view ever witnessed!

Left behind on the road, the big car came to a stop. Not for the first time since the Osmonds arrived in Hawaii, the Kruse-Wong team felt the sting of defeat!

In Suite 108, Sid paced up and down. "Al, where *could* they have gone? Donny knows we had wardrobe fittings scheduled." He suddenly stopped. "It's that Tricia! Spending a whole morning seeing Hawaii with her wasn't enough. No! They're probably out guzzling pineapple juice right this minute."

"Or—do you think coconut milk?" Al asked. "It's pretty good. Or maybe—"

The door flung open. Donny, battered, dirty, clothes torn, came into the room. Right behind him came Marie, just as smudged and even more rumpled than her brother.

"Is this some kind of makeup you've thought up for your first Hawaiian concert?" Sid asked angrily. "Where've you two been? Marie, if this is your idea of 'exploring Hawaii,' I wish—"

"Sid—wait a minute," Donny interrupted. "We were on a motorbike when this black car came after us."

"Don't tell me," Sid snapped. "It was Tricia trying to catch up with you. Wow! Some women just can't take rejection! Why were you on a motorbike in the first place?"

"Will you *listen?* There were three gunmen in that car. They tried to drive us off the road. And they *shot* at us."

"And," Marie added, "if Donny hadn't short-cut down a hill right into somebody's backyard, we'd be goners right now!"

Sid's face changed. "Are you saying . . . someone tried to kill you?" he asked slowly.

"Maybe it was backfiring instead of gunshots," Al said, trying to cheer up everybody.

Sid looked from Donny to Marie. The old Osmond sparkle just wasn't there. He strode to the telephone. "Well, this settles it! I'm going to cancel the concert and get you two out on the next plane!"

Donny stopped him. "No, Sid. Marie and I talked it over on the way back. We want to do this concert."

"Yes, Sid," Marie said earnestly. "Whatever they're trying to do, we're not going to be scared off."

Sid hesitated. "Hey, look kids, I mean—"

"It's important to us," Donny said quietly.

she's got protection." Proudly he circled thumb and index finger to give Marie that "everything's-under-control" feeling. Poor Marie!

Sid looked cheerfully over at the stonefaced "policeman." His cheerful expression faded. "A policeman with hearing aids?" Sid glanced down at the "officer's" shoes. His heart jumped! Sandals! No police officer would dare wear anything but regulation shoes. Slowly, he backed away, then made a frantic dash for another uniformed officer. "Get the lieutenant. Quick!" he whispered. "They're *here*. Back there in the wings. One of 'em."

"Who's back there?"

Sid had no time to explain. Snatching up the officer's walkie-talkie, he burbled, "Mayday! Mayday! There's an army of 'em backstage."

As Lieutenant Alecki's men moved in on both wings, Mr. Wong came peering around a pillar. Swiftly, he eased away. It was plain to him that the entire Kruse-Wong team were benched for the rest of the game! He hurried off to give Coach Kruse the bad news. As far as Coach Wong was concerned, the Osmond concert was over!

On the deserted backstage, Donny, Marie, and Sid waited for Lieutenant Alecki. "It was a fine performance, kids," Sid said. "Nobody would

Sid put down the phone. "Well, okay," he said slowly. "But we're not selling any more tickets. We're gonna fill up the rest of the place with cops."

CHAPTER 9

~~~~~~~~~~~~~~~~~~~~~~~~~~~~~~~~~~

PROFESSOR KRUSE AND Mr. Wong, in front-row seats, twisted around to watch the concert hall filling up. Tricia, also in the center section, met the Professor's ice-cold glance as it swept the audience. She smiled confidently and noticed his companion was Mr. Wong.

The Professor looked away. "I didn't know so many people attended these things. Did you, Wong?"

Mr. Wong shrugged. "I never knew uniformed police with walkie-talkies attended."

"Let us not give *them* a thought," the Professor sneered. "This time, we have everything under control."

Out in the lobby, Sid wasn't so sure that *he*

had everything under control. "Are you *sure* the kids will be okay?" he asked Lieutenant Alecki for the fifth time.

The Lieutenant nodded. "I've got men all over the place. They're as safe as if they were in their own suite."

"Great! Marie got mugged in her own room."

Lieutenant Alecki sighed. "Why don't you go backstage, sir?"

"Why? Is that a more comfortable place to get shot?" But he cast a last worried glance around and took the Lieutenant's advice.

Backstage, dancers, technicians and everybody else milled about. As a makeup man put final touches on Marie's face, Donny walked up. He squeezed her shoulders. "Frightened?"

"No."

"How about terrified?"

"That's closer," Marie answered.

There was a loud drumroll. Lights dimmed. And from the wings, Sid watched, wishing with all his heart he hadn't given in to Donny and Marie. "Those kids should be heading for a plane —not for a stage," he muttered nervously to a burly policeman standing next to him.

In the audience, Tricia glanced again in the direction of the Professor. Now the seat beside him was empty. She frowned. Then onstage, out bounced Donny and Marie, and Tricia joined the welcoming applause.

Marie never looked prettier. Donny's big smile had never been so appealing. The fans loved it! Marie whirled toward the wing where she knew Sid would be watching. And suddenly, beneath the makeup, color drained from her face. *That policeman!* Rapidly she whirled to face the other wing. Two more uniformed police—*and now she knew who'd been in that big black car! Three phony policemen!*

The song ended. Donny, about to bow, felt Marie's hand clutch his elbow. She signaled the band. There was nothing for Donny to do but go into another chorus, singing his head off.

But when Marie led off for a *third* reprise, Donny was not the only one puzzled. Dancers were confused. Sid was frowning, and Ito, Mickey, and J. L. were most puzzled of all. Donny glanced at his sister. Fast as lightning, and like a child playing "bang-bang," Marie got her message over to him as her fingers shaped a "shoot-'em-up," and her head nodded first toward one wing, then the other.

With extra-special Osmond enthusiasm, Donny flung himself into a third go of song and dance. But Sid's worried eye had also caught Marie's pantomime. "Poor kid! She's scared. Here!" he pushed Ito forward. "Officer, you stand where she can see you so she'll know have guessed what was going on up here. The fans loved the show."

For once, fans didn't seem so important to Donny and Marie as the arrival of Lieutenant Alecki. Donny hurried over as the Lieutenant came in the door. What'd they say?" he asked eagerly.

"They wouldn't talk."

Sid rushed up. "Didn't you find out *anything?*"

"Not from the interrogation," replied the Lieutenant. He reached into his pocket and brought out a folded sheet. "But we did find this on one of them."

Eagerly the three watched as Lieutenant Alecki spread out the creased paper. "It's part of an old Naval map of the Islands—dating back to 1941. Mean anything to you?"

"Nineteen forty-one!" Marie exclaimed. "We weren't even born then."

"It's like a map from an old John Wayne movie," Sid said glumly. "That's all you got? This is it?"

"Donny! Look!" Marie bent excitedly over the map. Her necklace dangled forward. "See the tip of that island?"

"So?"

Swiftly, she lifted the pendant. "It's the same shape as the pendant! Here!" She took it off. "Hold it over the map. *It just matches!*"

Donny fiddled the pendant into position. "This edge does seem to match the shoreline."

Lieutenant Alecki looked doubtful. "Could be coincidence."

But Marie was off and running with her discovery. "See, Lieutenant? The tip of the pendant points right there. The necklace *locates* something! But what?"

"Maybe a hockshop," Sid said wearily. "Hey. Let's call it a night."

Lieutenant Alecki didn't seem to hear that. He stared at the pendant and then at the map and frowned. "But that island is miles out in the ocean."

Marie bobbed her head. "What if it is? Lieutenant, after all this, I've just got to go look."

The Lieutenant laughed. "Okay. You may be disappointed. But I have a boat and scuba gear. And I'll be glad to take you out there in the morning."

Donny spanked his hands together. "Great! You're on!"

Sid frowned. "I don't know . . . Maybe—"

"Oh, Sid!" Marie exclaimed. "What can happen? It'll just be a nice ride."

Sid shook his head. "That's what they told Al Capone."

Donny laughed. "That's what gangsters said. But Sid—we're the *good* guys. Ask anybody!"

CHAPTER 10

~~~~~~~~~~~~~~~~~~~~~~~~~~~~~~~~~~

MORNING WAS SO beautiful that Sid forgot his gloomy feelings of the night before. In honor of the cruise in Lieutenant Alecki's boat, he turned up at the dock looking like an admiral —or at least a skipper in his snowy whites and a captain's yatching cap.

But by the time Lieutenant Alecki was ready to drop anchor far offshore, Sid was back in one of his best worrying moods. He watched anxiously as Donny and the lieutenant got into wet suits and checked the scuba gear.

"Donny," he said, "you know how Marie enjoys being with you. Maybe it would be better if you didn't dive."

"Certainly he'll dive!" Marie exclaimed.

"Really, Sid—you must have read somewhere about how important the buddy system is."

"That's what I'm talking about," Sid replied promptly. "The buddy system."

Donny grinned. "Wrong buddies!" he called over. "Ready, Lieutenant?"

"Ready."

Before Sid's anxious eyes, the two disappeared. And the blue Pacific plopped as gently against Lieutenant Alecki's boat as though one half of the Donny and Marie show was not hidden in its depths.

"Isn't this exciting!" Marie exclaimed. "I know they're going to find something *big!*"

Sid clenched his hands. "I just hope it doesn't have teeth."

"Sid—will you *stop* it? Check your watch. Do something. They'll be up in just minutes. Stop worrying!"

But, as the minutes went by, it seemed to Sid as though Donny and the Lieutenant were taking enough time to discover the shores of China.

Donny *was* discovering something—not twenty feet out from the drifting hull of Lieutenant Alecki's power boat. He pointed downward. There, in the strange green light of the undersea world, a submarine rested on the ocean floor.

The Lieutenant nodded, beckoned Donny, and together they started down, down. Schools of small fish circled about not seeming the least alarmed by the divers' arrival on the barnacle-encrusted surface of the sub. The Lieutenant signaled Donny to wait, and he disappeared through the open hatch.

Up above, Sid was ready to explode. "What's taking them so long?"

"Guess they haven't found anything," Marie sighed in disappointment.

"Well, let's *hope* they haven't found anything!" Sid snapped.

Behind them, Donny and Lieutenant Alecki cut the surface. Each placed a moss-covered metal bar on the diving platform. Donny removed his mouthpiece. "Sid! Marie!"

"Donny!" They rushed over. "What are they? What'd you find?"

"A sunken World War II American submarine."

"With a cargo of gold bars," Lieutenant Alecki added.

Sid was stunned. "Gold bars!"

The Lieutenant climbed aboard. "There's a fortune down there."

Marie was jumping in excitement. "I *knew* it! I knew my necklace was *important*. Did you hear that, Sid? *Gold bars!*"

Sid blinked. "Other kids go diving. They bring up tin cans. He comes up with gold bricks!"

"Donny," the Lieutenant asked. "Want to rest or should we get some more?"

"You listen to the Lieutenant, Donny," Sid ordered. "Remember, you're a fragile kid. Don't overdo. Ten or twenty bars at a time are plenty."

Donny grinned at Lieutenant Alecki. "Let's go," he said.

Neither Marie nor Sid had bothered to notice a sizable power boat swinging at anchor over in the distance. But two pairs of eyes on board were keeping a steady watch on them.

Mr. Wong lowered his binoculars. "Excellent. They're going down for the rest of it."

Professor Kruse beamed. "Your plan was most ingenious . . . to have them find the map and do all the work for us."

Mr. Wong shrugged. "Of course, it did mean sacrificing our three associates."

"Yes. A pity. The boys won't be able to share the fortune."

Mr. Wong's eyes glittered. He nodded toward Lieutenant Alecki's boat. "Alas! Neither will they."

By the time gold bars were stacked high on the diving platform, the two thugs serving as crewmen on Mr. Wong's boat were ready for action. Wearing scuba gear and carrying spearguns, they took their position on the side deck.

At the controls, Mr. Wong called out, "It's all

aboard!" Throttle open, the powerful boat surged forward.

Unaware that he now had a real reason to worry, Sid talked excitedly with Marie. "Okay, say eight hundred pounds at one hundred ninety dollars an ounce." He threw up his hands. "I can't do it without paper and pencil." He hurried into the cabin, leaving Marie chuckling.

She looked across the water. "Hey, another boat, Lieutenant," she said.

Lieutenant Alecki hardly bothered to look. He shrugged. "Donny, let's get the anchor up."

Shielded by the deckhouse, the two divers on the passing boat slipped into the water unnoticed by anyone aboard the Lieutenant's boat. Marie was busy taking pictures of the gold bars while Donny was stowing the anchor, and Lieutenant Alecki was starting the engine. All were thunderstruck when a tough voice rang out— "Everyone over here. Easy now!"

Out of nowhere, two menacing figures stood on deck. Armed with spearguns, they took instant command. The Lieutenant and the two Osmonds were herded together. And in the background Mr. Wong's boat swung sharply, making a fast approach.

"It's Professor Kruse!" Marie whispered. "The man from the museum!"

Any hope that the Professor had come to their rescue didn't last long—not when the boat tied up alongside and the Professor waved his Lüger at them. "You will transfer the gold to this vessel," he shouted. "Then you will return to your boat."

Mr. Wong popped into view. "But you will not return for long! We shall leave this behind." He grinned threateningly and motioned to a Kawasaki jet ski floating below.

It didn't look like any jet ski the Osmonds had seen before. Like a motorcycle mounted on a surfboard, this model had an extra feature—a small torpedo mounted at the front!

Mr. Wong's eyes flickered evil. "You will note an explosive charge and a homing device to guide it to the nearest target. *You!*"

One of the two boarding thugs hurried up to the rail. "I took care of their radio and got the gun in the wheelhouse."

"Very good," said Professor Kruse. "Now the gentleman in the cabin—he will assist in unloading the gold bars." He motioned to the Lieutenant. "Get him."

Lieutenant Alecki made a slight tilt of eye. Donny's glance followed. He saw a small fire hatchet stowed in a bracket . . . and then the line connecting the boats.

"Go! Go!" Professor Kruse yelled.

The Lieutenant stepped to the companionway. "Sid," he called down.

Sid, eyes on the sheet of paper he held, appeared. "I think I've got a good estimate here," he said without glancing up. "Say eight hundred pounds at a hundred ninety dollars an ounce. That's about two and a half million, which divided by four . . . well, really, *three* ways, Donny and Marie are a team."

For the moment the Professor and Mr. Wong were spellbound by this interesting financial information. And the Lieutenant acted. Leaping forward, he grabbed the throttles. As the boat lurched forward, the two hired thugs catapulted backward into the water. Donny grabbed the hatchet and brought it down across the tautline connecting the two boats. He grabbed Marie and held her close to the deck. Alas! Nobody held the financial wizard in the yachting cap! Over he went, unseen by anyone. Lieutenant Alecki raced to the wheelhouse.

The two thugs climbed back aboard Mr. Wong's boat. It zoomed off in hot pursuit as Sid, still wearing a now sodden captain's hat, floundered to the surface. In total confusion, he blinked at the *two* departing boats. "Don't get sore, Donny," he yelled. "We'll split it four ways!"

To his dismay, Lieutenant Alecki's boat kept right on going—at top speed. For all practical purposes, Sid was alone and adrift on the broad Pacific. Forlornly, he reached out and clutched the only man-made thing in sight—the torpedo-armed jet ski.

To make less of a target in case of gunfire, Donny and Marie both huddled close to the deck. "Sid," Donny shouted, "Get down on the deck!" He turned. "Sid?"

Edging back, he peered over the stern. "We've got to go back!" he shouted. "Sid fell off!"

"Sid!" Marie scrambled back. She heaved a giant sigh. "He's okay, Donny. See? He's getting on the jet ski."

Donny paled. *"The jet ski!* Marie! That torpedo! If he runs into anything, it'll blow up. *And he doesn't know it."*

CHAPTER 11

~~~~~~

IT WAS A SEAGOING parade. Lieutenant Alecki now led the way, followed by Mr. Wong's boat, followed by that lone sea gull of the Pacific—Sid, astride the speedy little Kawasaki.

And Sid was closing in. Lost in the throb of powerful engines, his voice shrilled out, "Hey! Wherever you are—stop! Stop and get me. *Please.*"

Up ahead the two thugs kept on firing at the Lieutenant's boat, and no one aboard was looking astern to see the jet ski fast closing the gap.

But Donny, in the lead craft, peered back anxiously. "They're gonna catch us. Marie, get down to the cabin!"

Wong, at the helm, was brimming with evil glee. "Good," he shouted. "We've got 'em!"

Not quite. A shout arose from alongside. "All I want is a ride in. I'll pay. I'm rich."

Before his horrified eyes the Kawasaki made a swerve straight for the boat. Mr. Wong swore a mighty Chinese oath. Professor Kruse screeched, "Turn! Turn!" And with an enormous spin of the wheel, Mr. Wong swung his boat seaward.

At the rail of the lieutenant's boat Donny and Marie cheered. "Good old Sid! Another minute and they'd have been on us!"

Good old Sid was not giving up his hopes for seagoing hitchhiking. He swung the jet ski toward the Lieutenant's boat. "Donny! Marie! It's me. Sid! Wait!"

In the wheelhouse the Lieutenant knew just how Mr. Wong must have felt. Sid, with deadly aim, whizzed the jet ski toward them. Lieutenant Alecki spun the wheel.

"Hey!" Donny shouted. "We're heading straight for that Kruse guy!"

"What choice have we got?" the Lieutenant shouted back.

"DONNNNNNYYY!" the desperate Sid shouted. "Wait!"

Nothing could have given Mr. Wong more pleasure than the sight of the Kawasaki plunging onward, almost amidships of the Lieutenant's boat. "That wonderful fool is delivering the gold right back to us!" he crowed.

"Not yet!" Professor Kruse screeched.

And no wonder! The Lieutenant, racing his boat out of Sid's target range, was pulling abreast of the Wong craft. And now *dead ahead* of boat boats, Sid, determined to catch a ride back to Honolulu, made a return zoom.

"Turn!" screamed the Professor.

"Turn!" screamed Donny.

And as each craft veered wildly, Wong heading out to sea and the Lieutenant aiming landward, Sid went bounding through the propeller gap.

He nearly burst into tears. "I knew it. They never liked me."

But there was nothing to do but swallow his pride and make one more try. Bravely, he changed course and went leaping through the foaming, fan-shaped wake of the Lieutenant's boat. "All right, Donny! *Five* percent. *Five* percent."

Marie, thoughts of golden treasure gone from her head, gripped the rail. "Donny! What are we going to do? We can't leave Sid out here."

"Maybe he'll run out of gas," Donny said, not too hopefully. "Except *we'll* probably run out of gas before he does."

"So what'll we *do?*"

Above the pound of the engines came the

heavy *chop-chop* of a helicopter. And as it neared them, a ladder began trailing downward in the wind. A face appeared in the bubble. "Donny! Marie!"

"It's *Tricia!*" Donny exclaimed. "What's she doing up there?"

"Inviting you to come up," Marie answered quickly. "Tell her to get Sid instead."

"Good idea."

Now the ladder swung just above the deck. Donny grabbed it.

"Get Sid! Sid!" he shouted, pointing toward the churning wake and the Kawasaki.

Tricia nodded. Instantly the copter veered away. And instantly, Donny was lifted from the deck. To Marie's horror, her brother was looking more like a Hollywood stunt man than a Hollywood stunt man looked. Desperately, he clung to the lower rungs of the ladder. The Pacific never looked bigger.

And Mr. Wong and Professor Kruse never looked more pleased. "It's just a rescue chopper. By the time it takes those two ashore, we'll have the other boat *and* the gold."

Professor Kruse nodded happily. "This is splendid! I believe they're planning to take that fool off the jet ski. High time!"

The Professor was right. Dangling by one hand, Donny reached down. "Sid! Grab the ladder! Grab it!"

Friends again! Sid joyfully reached up, giving the jet ski controls a passing kick. The copter jerked up, the jet ski jerked around, and in one glorious moment the situation took a turn for the worse.

Professor Kruse, Mr. Wong, and their two hired thugs changed to four blocks of ice. Like a deadly ice pick, the torpedo charge stabbed through the water.

"Jump!" Mr. Wong screamed in Chinese.

Even with no knowledge of the language, his companions immediately obeyed. A split second later there was a deafening explosion as the Kawasaki crashed into the ill-fated boat.

From his lookout point on the ladder rung, Sid had an excellent view of a scene he couldn't believe—four men bobbing about in the Pacific dodging flying debris. "And to think I might have been on that boat!" he gasped into the wind.

CHAPTER 12

IT WAS "*ALOHA* time" at the airport terminal. Donny and Marie watched Sid hurrying over to the luggage counter.

Marie sighed. "You know, Donny, we've seen a very unusual event."

"We sure have. Which one do you have in mind?"

"Sid. Do you realize we saw him *for the first time* get his mind off his work?"

Donny laughed. "And get his mind off those gold bricks too. I guess by now, though, he's figuring the Government should cancel his taxes for life."

"Well—we *did* do a very good deed," Marie said.

"Come on, Maria. *We* didn't do it. Your necklace did it."

"Hi, there!" a voice called out gaily. Beautiful, smiling, and utterly spotless in her Naval Officer's uniform, Tricia walked up to them.

"Oh, *hi!*" Donny beamed. "You taking the same flight?"

"No. I came to say 'aloha,' and wish you luck," Tricia replied.

"Oh." Donny's voice fell. "Well, thanks, Tricia. That's awfully nice of you."

"And thanks from me, too," Marie said. "Tricia, there's been something I've been dying to ask you since yesterday. Why weren't you in your Navy uniform until practically right this minute? I mean—well, *I* would have been. They're so good-looking."

Tricia laughed. "Well, the Navy more or less said, 'Tricia, wear your own clothes. You're on special duty.' You see, that necklace was my assignment. I'd been following it for over a year. The Navy knew it could lead us to that sub. But we couldn't figure out *how*. So when I heard you'd gone diving with Lieutenant Alecki, I figured . . . Police? Marie? Necklace? *Diving?* And I was pretty sure something was up—or maybe I should say *down*."

Marie sighed. "Thanks forever for figuring right."

"Maybe we could thank you over on the

mainland, too," Donny suggested. "Do you ever get over there?"

"I'm there most of the time," Tricia replied.

"Oh?" Donny's eyes sparkled. "Then maybe we could get together? You could come visit our television show, then I could show you around."

"Thank you! My husband would love it. He's a great fan of yours."

Donny looked so stunned that Marie leaped into the two-way conversation. "Donny would love to show you *both* around." She smiled up at her brother. "Anything for the fans. Right, Donny?"

"Then maybe we'll see you," Tricia said. "It'd be fun."

After that, "aloha" seemed the best thing to say, and they waved Tricia good-bye.

Marie turned to a forlorn Donny. "Hey, I'm sorry. Honest. But you'll get over it. There are *lots* of—"

"No, Marie. She was *it*. You'll know it when it happens to you. I'll probably be a very old man before I can ever look at another girl."

"Excuse me." A very pretty girl bobbed into view. She held out an autograph book and a pen. "Would you?" she asked Donny. "I couldn't believe it when I found out we were going to be on the same plane."

Donny took the pen and book. "Are you

traveling with your husband?" he asked politely.

"No. I'm not married."

"Oh. Your boyfriend, then?"

"No," she smiled, reaching for the pen. "Thank you."

"—Er. Could I help you with that carryon bag?"

"Oh. *Thank* you."

Donny's smile flashed. "It's Gate Three. Let's go."

Marie watched the two walk away. "Well! The Invisible Woman! That's me," she muttered.

Sid hurried up. "Come on, Gate Three. Where's—"

Marie grinned. "Where's the 'very old man'?"

"What d'y mean? What very old man? I meant Donny."

"So did I." She giggled. "Tell you all about it sometime."

At Gate Three, Marie turned and looked back. "Aloha, Hawaii," she said happily. "It's been *great!*"

Outstanding Laurel-Leaf Fiction for Young Adult Readers

☐ **A LITTLE DEMONSTRATION OF AFFECTION**
  Elizabeth Winthrop   **$1.25**
A 15-year-old girl and her older brother find themselves turning to each other to share their deepest emotions.

☐ **M.C. HIGGINS THE GREAT**
  Virginia Hamilton   **$1.25**
Winner of the Newbery Medal, the National Book Award and the Boston Globe-Horn Book Award, this novel follows M.C. Higgins' growing awareness that both choice and action lie within his power.

☐ **PORTRAIT OF JENNIE**
  Robert Nathan   **$1.25**
Robert Nathan interweaves touching and profound portraits of all his characters with one of the most beautiful love stories ever told.

☐ **THE MEAT IN THE SANDWICH**
  Alice Bach   **$1.25**
Mike Lefcourt dreams of being a star athlete, but when hockey season ends, Mike learns that victory and defeat become hopelessly mixed up.

☐ **Z FOR ZACHARIAH**
  Robert C. O'Brien   **$1.25**
This winner of an Edgar Award from the Mystery Writers of America portrays a young girl who was the only human being left alive after nuclear doomsday—or so she thought.

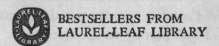 **BESTSELLERS FROM LAUREL-LEAF LIBRARY**

☐ **ARE YOU THERE, GOD? IT'S ME, MARGARET**
by Judy Blume $1.25 0419-39

☐ **THE BOY WHO COULD MAKE HIMSELF DISAPPEAR** by Kin Platt $1.25 0837-25

☐ **THE CHOCOLATE WAR**
by Robert Cormier $1.25 4459-08

☐ **DEENIE** by Judy Blume $1.25 3259-02

☐ **DURANGO STREET**
by Frank Bonham $1.25 2183-13

☐ **FAIR DAY, AND ANOTHER STEP BEGUN**
by Katie Letcher Lyle $1.25 5968-09

☐ **IF I LOVE YOU, AM I TRAPPED FOREVER?**
by M. E. Kerr $1.25 4320-05

☐ **I'LL GET THERE, IT BETTER BE WORTH THE TRIP** by John Donovan ... $1.25 3980-08

☐ **I'M REALLY DRAGGED BUT NOTHING GETS ME DOWN** by Nat Hentoff .... 95¢ 3988-26

☐ **I WILL GO BAREFOOT ALL SUMMER FOR YOU**
by Katie Letcher Lyle $1.25 4327-08

☐ **JANE EMILY** by Patricia Clapp .... 75¢ 4185-09

☐ **THE OUTSIDERS** by S. E. Hinton $1.25 6769-40

☐ **THE PIGMAN** by Paul Zindel $1.25 6970-11

☐ **THAT WAS THEN, THIS IS NOW**
by S. E. Hinton $1.25 8652-12

MARTYN WAKELIN

Discovering
English Dialects

To Kostas,
Christmas 1989.

Picked this up at
Plimoth Plantation
for you, Oct. 1989.

Merry Christmas,
Cindy, Oliver,
Nicola + even
Booster.

SHIRE PUBLICATIONS LTD

ACKNOWLEDGEMENTS

Many people have generously contributed to the preparation of this book; thanks are especially due to the following: Mr J. Banks, Mr M. V. Barry, Dr P. Wright, Mr C. S. Upton; Dr P. Trudgill, Mr J. Milroy, Mrs B. Neale, Dr J. D. A. Widdowson, Mr R. Dobson, Mr G. Williams, Mr D. Parry, Miss R. Franklin, Mr K. G. Spencer, Mr P. M. Tilling, Miss N. Dawson, Mr O. Padel, Mr R. F. Wakelin.

I thank the following for permission to use previously published material: Mr S. F. Sanderson, for use of the *Survey of English Dialects* base map; the Board of Management of the Athlone Press for maps 1 and 3 (from M. F. Wakelin, *English Dialects*, 2nd ed., 1977, pp. 87 and 134, respectively) and map 4 (from M. F. Wakelin (ed.), *Patterns in the Folk Speech of the British Isles*, 1972, p. 186); the Secretary and Council of the Yorkshire Dialect Society for map 2 (F. Rohrer, *Transactions*, part 50 (1950), p. 34), map 9 (E. Kolb, *Transactions*, part 65 (1965), p. 12) and fig. 4 (P. Wright , *Transactions*, part 66 (1966), p. 42); Leicester University Press for map 5 (from M. F. Wakelin, *Language and History in Cornwall*, 1975, p. 178); A. Brown and Sons for map 7 (from K. G. Spencer, *The Lapwing in Britain*, 1953, p. 108); Oxford University Press for map 8 (from I. and P. Opie, *The Lore and Language of Schoolchildren*, 1959, p. 177); Andre Deutsch for map 10 (from G. L. Brook, *English Dialects*, 2nd. ed., 1965, p. 62); J. M. Dent and Sons for figs. 1 (from M. Hartley and J. Ingilby, *Life and Tradition in the Yorkshire Dales*, 1968, p. 33) and 6 (from M. Hartley and J. Ingilby, *The Yorkshire Dales*, 1956, p. 261); Faber and Faber for fig. 2 (from G. Ewart Evans, *The Horse in the Furrow*, 1960, p. 136; illustration by C. F. Tunnicliffe); The Federation of Old Cornwall Societies and the executor of the late Miss Mary Mills for fig. 3 (from *Old Cornwall*, Vol. 8, No. 3 (1974), p. 141); Cambridge University Press for fig. 5 (from A. Arber, *Herbals, their Origin and Evolution*, 1912, p. 147).

Printed in Great Britain by C. I. Thomas & Sons (Haverfordwest) Ltd, Press Buildings, Merlins Bridge, Haverfordwest, Dyfed.

Contents

ABBREVIATIONS

Corn.	Cornish
EDS	English Dialect Society
Fr	French
(M)Du	(Middle) Dutch
ME	Middle English
(M)LG	(Middle) Low German
OE	Old English
OF	Old French
ON	Old Norse
ONF	Old Northern French
RSE	Received Standard English
SED	*Survey of English Dialects*
*	Hypothetical, reconstructed form (i.e. unrecorded, but assumed to have once existed)

Single or double letters in bold type indicate *sounds*, not spellings. Note especially the following:

a	as in *cat*
ah	as in *grass*
aw	as in *law*
ay	as in *late*
dh	as in *then*
é	as in Fr *té*
ea	as in *air* (approx.)
ee	as in *see*
i (long)	as in *fine*
ia	as in *ear* (approx.)
oo	as in *good* or *boot*
ooa	as in *doer* (approx.)
uh	as in *rust*
zh	as in *measure*

3

1. What are dialects?

We may usefully define *dialects* as sub-forms of languages which are, in general, mutually comprehensible, *languages* as forms which are not. The forms of speech local, say, to Wiltshire and North Yorkshire are dialect because, even though the local types of speech found in these counties are very different from each other, the people who use one can — in the main — be understood by people who use the other. This is not so with the forms of speech used in England and Germany, which are thus languages, not dialects. The Wiltshire man who says 'How be 'ee gwine ("going") on?' can be understood by the North Yorkshire man, with his 'Hoo ("how") is thou?' (however, compare, also from the north, 'What fettle?'!), but German 'Wie geht es Ihnen?' is only comprehensible to English people when they have learned German. Languages have progressed one stage further than dialects in their historical development.

Within any language there are likely to be different types of dialects. In English we need to note three in particular. These are:

(1) The old regional dialects of countryside and town

In their most complete form these are spoken best by older men and women who have lived in their own area all their lives, but middle-aged people and children frequently speak regional dialect to varying extents too. Often these latter use intermediate varieties, i.e. a basis of Standard English *influenced by* the dialect of their early years or their more recent surroundings, or a basis of dialect *influenced by* the Standard English they have adopted or are trying to adopt. For example, a native speaker of northern regional English may have become modified in the direction of Standard English so far as to lose some of his most distinctive 'native' sounds, such as **oo** in *mother, but,* replacing this by Standard English **uh.** Contrariwise, a person from the West Midlands who has long assumed a Standard English form of speech may be perfect in it except that he retains just one sound, e.g. the **g** sound at the end of words like *sing* and *hang.*

The dialects in their completest forms are best heard in countryside villages and hamlets and often appear in a broken-down form in the larger towns. Although there is bound to be a basis of, say, Yorkshire dialect in cities like Leeds, Bradford, Sheffield and York, over the years, perhaps mainly owing to influxes of industrial workers from all over Britain, such city dialects have become mixed not only with Standard English but also with other strains and thus differ to varying extents from the language of the surrounding countryside. (For example, it has already been shown that Norwich city dialect has been influenced by that of London.) Within a city, too, there may be several sub-

4

varieties, especially in the larger industrial complexes. Towns like Bradford and Corby are of special interest in this respect because of their history of mixed populations (West Indians in Bradford, Scots and Irish in Corby). It is in the cities that we can expect new syntheses of types of speech to emerge out of old varieties, and in this sense dialect is not dying at all, as it is sometimes said to be.

When discussing dialect, we shall find it necessary to distinguish various 'levels' — those of sounds or pronunciation, vocabulary and grammar — and examples of these in regional dialect are:

Sounds: The pronunciation of, e.g., *fish, sing, think, shall* in the south-west of England with initial **v, z, dh, zh;** the northern and midland use of an **oo** sound (as in Standard English *put*) in words like *mother, but.*

Vocabulary: *Gawp* 'stare', *nesh* 'soft', *bonny* 'pretty', *beck* 'stream' in parts of the north and midlands; *soak* 'make' (the tea) and *bladder* 'blister' in the south-west; *tundish* 'funnel', *pool* 'pond', *grains* 'dregs' in the west.

Grammar: The widespread use of the old pronouns *thou, thee, thy*, etc, and of *hisn, hern, ourn, yourn, theirn* 'his, hers, ours, yours, theirs'; the western forms of the verb *to be — I be, I bain't* ('I'm not'), etc.

Intonation. Intonation patterns (the different ways in which the voice rises and falls) in dialect have not yet been sufficiently studied, but we may draw attention to the very distinctive varieties of these to be found in the north (Tyne and Wear, etc), in East Anglia and in Cornwall. No doubt others also deserve attention.

Dialects outside England. This book is about regional dialect spoken in England; the English dialect of Wales, Scotland, Northern Ireland and the Isle of Man is not dealt with, because — apart from lack of space and the slightly complicating factor of the special histories of these areas — their dialects are not yet sufficiently documented to allow us to make general statements, and any treatment would inevitably have been scrappy and inconsistent. However, references are given to relevant sources of information, which are happily increasing, and it is hoped that the interested reader will consult these for himself.

(2) Social dialects

There is variation in speech between people of different classes as much as there is between people of different areas. At one end of this scale there is an ill-defined type of speech, a complex of numerous very similar varieties loosely held together in what we call Received Standard English (RSE), mainly in use among professional and educated classes (this includes affected varieties, e.g. the 'Oxford accent', which has nothing to do with Oxford itself); at the other end is a type of speech which usually still includes a substantial element of local dialect and perhaps a lot of slang. And in between these two we can hear the infinitely varied shades of speech from 'modified regional' at one end to 'modified RSE' at the other. This 'scale' of speech-types is likely to be best observed in large towns. We shall not be dealing very much with social variation in this book, but examples from either end of this scale are:

Sounds: Loss of **h** as in *'urt, 'ome, 'appy; a* (RSE *an*) before a vowel, as in *a egg, a 'andkerchief;* **n** (RSE **ng**) e.g. in *walking, going;* other more localised features, e.g. **a** (RSE **aw**) in *water* (i.e. *watter*); **ay** (RSE **ee**) in *tea* (i.e. *tay*).

Vocabulary: *Summat* (i.e. *somewhat;* RSE *something*); *as* and *what* (RSE *that* or *who*), as in 'the dog what I saw', 'someone as often goes there'; *learn* (RSE *teach*) — 'he learned me French', etc.

Grammar: Use of *our* (RSE *my*), *us* (RSE *me*) — 'give it us'; *ain't* (RSE *aren't*); *-s* ending in all parts of verbs — *I sings, we goes* (RSE has *-s* only after *he, she* or *it* or a singular subject); double negation — 'I ain't done nothing'.

And at all these levels, sounds, vocabulary and grammar, as has already been said, one end of the scale tends to retain local pronunciations, words and grammar, while RSE — essentially a non-local type of speech — loses them.

(3) Occupational dialects

These consist mainly of the specialised vocabularies used in different industries and occupations such as the aeroplane industry, the theatre, mining, barrel-making and so on. This sort of language, especially when it has no regional variation, is 'technical jargon' as well as dialect. Sometimes, however, there is a regional variation, as we can see from fishing and mining terms. Examples are:

Fishing: A short stick used in net-making is called a *kebble* or *kibble* (north-west coasts); a *shuttle* (mainly north-eastern); a *shale* (Humberside, East Anglia); a *lace* (north Devon, Cornwall, Dorset); a *scandle* (south Cornwall).

Mining: Poor coal is called *brockens* or *splints* (Tyne and Wear); *bags* or *muck* (South Yorkshire); *mothering* (Avon); *clod* (Gloucestershire); *rubbishy stuff* (Salop); *burgy* (Greater Manchester); *rubbish* (Cumbria).

Spoken and written forms

A careful distinction must be made between spoken and written forms of language, which are by no means the same. Speech is not based on writing (although attempts have been made to bring this about); otherwise we should have to pronounce, for example, the *gh* written in *knight* and the *w* written in *wrong.*

All the dialectal varieties we have mentioned are found in spoken form, which is what we shall be mainly concerned with in this book, but their occurrence in written form is less regular. Up to about AD 1450 all English, both spoken and written, was local, dialectal, but the written forms of these varieties gradually died out under the influence of Standard English, which began to rise to prominence from about the fourteenth century, although they may still be found in local documents (wills, accounts, etc) until much later. From about the sixteenth century onwards they also began to reappear in specially written 'dialect literature', which was intended to display the characteristics of the spoken dialects. By the eighteenth century this type of literature had become a flood, which continued into the nineteenth, and it is still written today. Of a rather different nature is the incorporation of dialect words and imitated pronunciations into novels and plays to give a dramatic effect, a practice which goes as far back as Chaucer and continues today.

Written social varieties of English are also sometimes used for special effect in literature. Charles Dickens, for example, includes imitation of the speech of widely differing classes of people in his portrayals of nineteenth-century life, and an eminent predecessor is William Shakespeare, some of whose characters' speech is of a lower-class stratum.

Occupational dialects appear in writing too, but usually only in special circumstances, when an author wants to create a realistic effect and needs to do so by the use of technical terms proper to the occupation he is writing about. Nautical language, for example, was used for literary effect in English as early as the fourteenth-century poem *Patience* (a verse homily on the life of Jonah) and as recently as the nineteenth-century American novel *Moby Dick.*

---

2. Some regional features

This chapter aims to draw attention to some of the more significant or interesting pronunciations, dialectal words and grammatical features which are to be found up and down England today, especially those which show definite regional *distributions.* The features mentioned, one must remember, are most frequently found in the speech of older people who have spoken local dialect since their early days, but many of them can also be heard from younger people.

The north

Pronunciation

England is divided by two very important boundaries in pronunciation: (a) dialect speakers of all ages, both young and old, in the northern part of England traditionally use a short **a** sound in words of the *grass, laugh, path,* and *branch, dance* classes, while in the south it is lengthened — most notably, speakers of RSE use a long **ah** sound; (b) the same (northern) speakers use an **oo** sound (as in RSE *put*) in words like *cup, butter, rough,* while southern speakers and speakers of RSE use a much more open sound (approaching **a** in the south-east), without the lips being rounded. Map 1 shows that the boundaries separating short **a** from the lengthened types and **oo** from southern **uh** are not as far north as is sometimes thought. Sometimes, in an attempt to come into line with RSE, younger dialect speakers produce hybrid forms, using a sound somewhere between **oo** and **uh** in *butter,* etc.

Within the northern area shown on the map we find another important boundary, dividing the north proper from the north midlands. This now runs — it has apparently been northward moving for some time — from the mouth of the river Humber, roughly along the Ouse and Wharfe valleys, and out of north Lancashire via the Lune and Ribble valleys, and represents the boundary which in Anglo-Saxon times, probably running much further to the south, divided Northumbria from Mercia; it is therefore an extremely ancient ethnic as well as linguistic boundary. It is characterised by a group of features of pronunciation only the most important of which can be given here. One of the most striking of these is the use of a long **oo** (as in RSE *boot, loose*) in words like *brown, cow, house* (thus *broon, coo, hoose*). In many places this is now tending to be replaced either by the RSE diphthong or an imitation of it.

A similar line marks off another set of distinctive pronunciations, namely those of sounds approaching **ia** or RSE *ear,* sometimes **i-oo,** in words of the *boot, fool, goose, spoon* class, and sounds approaching **ia** or **ea** (the sound in RSE *air*) in the *bone, loaf, road* class. In both of these classes attempts have been made over the years to conform more closely to the RSE pronunciation, and in the second class this has resulted in a very distinctive and persistent sound made with the lips rounded (as in the vowels of French *peu* or *feuille*) in Northumberland, Tyne and Wear and north Durham.

North of the Humber, and as far south as Lincolnshire, words in the *coal, coat, foal, hole* class (whose vowel is distinct historically from that in *bone, loaf, road,* etc) traditionally have a diphthong rather like that found in RSE *doer,* with the rounded sound (above) occurring again in Northumberland, Tyne and

Map 1. *Some* and *chaff* (after *SED:* the numbered localities are those of the *Survey*).

Key: —— General southern limit of **oo** in *some.*
      - - - General southern limit of a short vowel in *chaff.*

(Older northern and midland **oo** in *some,* etc, had probably become **uh** as early as the fifteenth century in some dialects, and has probably existed in RSE since *c.* 1550; dialectal lengthening of **a** before **f, s** and **th** in the south started in the seventeenth century, **ah** being adopted into RSE probably from south-eastern dialects sometime in the eighteenth.)

9

Wear and north Durham.

More or less the same boundary as these divides Northumbrian **ee, ia** in *eat, speak*, etc, from north-midland **ay.**

Map 2 shows how these old features of pronunciation cluster, marking off the area north of the Humber as a very distinctive northern dialect area.

Further north still Northumberland, Tyne and Wear and their environs are characterised by the retention of initial **h,** both in words like *hat, help, hurry* and in words like *what, when, which.* Although it is kept in RSE, most dialects have now lost initial **h** (although it is also found strongly in Somerset and East Anglia), and all the dialects *and* RSE have now lost the aspiration in words beginning with the letters *wh*. It is all the more singular, then, that this small area has retained both.

It also features a pronunciation first remarked upon by Daniel

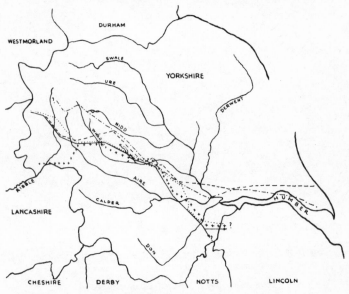

Map 2. Northern/north-midland boundaries.
   Key: southern limits of northern pronunciations:

··········	*coo* ('cow')
—·—·	*spian* ('spoon')
------	*bian* ('bone')
+++	*fooal* ('foal')
———	*iat* ('eat')

10

Defoe in his *Tour thro' the whole Island of Great Britain* (1724-7), namely the 'uvular' **r** (so called because made with the uvula at the back of the throat), sometimes known as the 'Northumbrian burr' or more popularly as the 'Geordie **r**' — what Defoe calls 'a hollow jarring in the throat'. Readers who wish to learn how to pronounce it should follow the instructions in Scott Dobson's excellent *Larn Yersel' Geordie* (Frank Graham, Newcastle, 1969)!

One or two features of pronunciation found in old, traditional dialect between the Humber and the small area we have just been considering remind us that this was an area of Scandinavian occupation. Although the region ultimately occupied by the medieval Norsemen extended very much further south than the river Humber (it comprised Anglo-Saxon Northumbria, East Anglia and Scandinavian Mercia), it is the north which now retains the most pervasive linguistic traces of their presence.

An example of possible Scandinavian influence on English pronunciation is the substitution of **sk** for **sh** in one or two words, e.g. *mask* 'mash' (i.e brew the tea) and (now obsolete) *skelf* 'shelf', *skift* 'shift', etc. The Scandinavians did not have the sound **sh** in their own dialects and substituted their nearest sound, which was **sk.**

A specially interesting word here is *pace-* (with loss of the **k**) or *paste-eggs*, the northern name for the eggs which children still dye and decorate at Easter time in Scotland, Ulster, the northern counties and north midlands (as well as on the Continent). The first part of this word is probably ON *páskar* 'Easter', which is in turn from Latin *pascha*. A traditional Northumbrian song, 'The Pitman's Courtship' (1818), runs:

> And to please the pit laddies at Easter
> A dishful of gilty paste eggs.

We do not hear of *pace-eggs* until 1579, according to the *OED*, but the custom is of ancient origin.

We also find substitution of **k** and **g** in words which in RSE have **ch** and **j**. This took place either by direct borrowing of the Scandinavian equivalent of the English word (e.g. *kirk* — ON *kirkja* — replaces *church* — OE *cirice*, whose *c*s were pronounced as **ch**) or by phonetic influence. Thus we find Scandinavian parallels to the RSE terms in *kirk* 'church', *kirn* 'churn', *birk* 'birch', for instance, all now somewhat obsolescent except in place-names (e.g. Kirkoswald, Bridekirk, Birkbeck); similarly *brig* 'bridge', *rig* 'ridge' (place-names: Brigstones, Brighouse, Brownriggs).

Vocabulary

Consideration of possible Scandinavian influence on northern sounds brings us to the question of northern vocabulary — although this does not imply that all or even most northern

Map 3. Scandinavian loan-words.
Key: ——— *steg*
.... *lea*
——— *ket*
– – – *stee*

vocabulary is derived from the medieval Norse dialects; much of it is as English in origin as is southern and midland vocabulary.

Many words, like *steg* 'gander' (ON *steggi, steggr*), *lea* 'scythe' (ON *lé*), *stee* 'ladder' (ON *stige*), *ket* 'rubbish' (ON *kjot*) are, as map 3 shows, spread over an area stretching diagonally right across northern England; to the north of this area, English words tend to predominate rather than Scandinavian ones, representing an area in which the Scandinavian presence was less strongly felt. Others — like *lop* 'flea' (probably ON *hloppa*), *lathe* 'barn' (ON *hlatha*), *sark* 'shirt' (ON *serkr*), *kay-fisted, -pawed* 'left-handed' (Danish *kei*) — occur now only in parts of this area, though they were probably once more widespread, while yet others, like *bairn* 'child' (perhaps ON *barn*, though maybe OE *bearn*), *beck* 'brook' (ON *bekkr*) and *neave* 'fist' (ON *hnefi*) are still widespread in parts outside this area. Some of these dialect words can also be found as elements in northern place-names (e.g. *lathe* in Silloth, *beck* in Beckwithshaw, Drybeck).

The Scandinavian element found in northern dialect is some indication of how much English, both dialectal and non-dialectal, owes to other languages. Such borrowing goes back to the earliest times, when the Anglo-Saxons took one or two words from their Celtic predecessors in England, words which are still current in dialect, like *brock* 'badger' (OE *broc*, from a Celtic source), now found only very occasionally though mainly in the north of England. The word *brat* 'apron', found in northern counties and occasionally in the north midlands, is probably from Old Irish *bratt* 'cloth', especially as a covering for the body, 'plaid, mantle, cloak', and is found in the north even as early as Old English times in the famous Northumbrian *Lindisfarne Gospels* (*c*. 950).

The foreign element in the vocabulary must not blind us to the richness of the native Anglo-Saxon contribution. Northern words like *wark* 'ache' (*teeth-wark, belly-wark;* OE *wærc*), *spelk* 'splinter' (OE *spelc*), *burn* 'stream' (OE *burna*), *ask, asker, askel, asgel, naskel,* etc 'newt' (OE *āthexe*), *nobutt,* i.e. 'nought but', 'only' (OE *nān + bē-ūtan*), *byre* (OE *bȳre*), *mistall* (OE *mēox* 'dung' + *stall*). *shippon* (OE *scypen*), all 'cow-house', *delve* (OE *delfan*) and *grave (OE grafan*), both 'dig' — all these are words firmly rooted in English soil from the beginning.

Much traditional vocabulary is thus still current in rural England, and in some industries the old words have apparently been pressed into new use: a Durham miner's snack is his *bait* and that of a Nottinghamshire miner his *snap* (from his *snap-bag*), both originally farmers' terms. The Sheffield steel industry uses words like *pens* for huge scrap-containers, and *strickle* as referring to the instrument used to smoothe the outside walls of a mould, perhaps transferred from its original usage referring to an instrument used for smoothing grain in a measure (OE *stricel*).

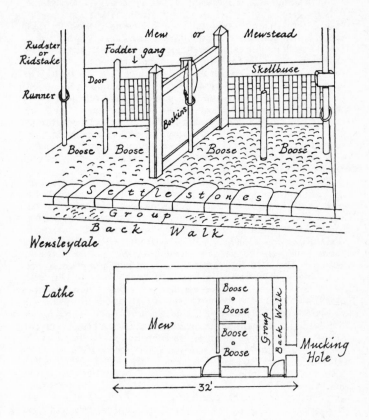

Fig. 1. The Wensleydale *lathe*. Note the terms *mew* and *mewstead* 'part of the barn where hay is kept' (OE *muga* + *stede*); *fodder gang* 'passage at head of cow-stall' (OE *fōdor* + *gang*); *boose* 'stall' (OE *·bōs*); *skell-buse* (or *-boose* 'partition'; cf. ON *skilja* 'to divide' + OE *·bōs*); *boskins* 'partitions' (OE *·bōs* + diminutive *-kin*); *rudster* and *ridstake* 'pole to which cattle are tied' (first part ? OE *wrǣd* 'band(age)'); *group* (or *groop* 'channel'; MDu *groepe*).

14

Grammar

Nouns. The older grammatical features of dialectal speech seem chiefly to be found in the south and west of England, but there are also some of interest in the north. In various parts of England nouns still have plurals formed in traditional dialect according to ancient methods, and in particular the so-called weak plurals still exist in some areas — i.e. forms like RSE *oxen,* derived from Anglo-Saxon times, with *-n* or *-en* added to the word to make the plural instead of *-s* or *-es. Shoon* 'shoes' is a northern example, stretching southwards, however, as far as Cheshire, Derbyshire and Staffordshire. *Een* 'eyes' likewise is still found as an old usage throughout the north and in some of the west-midland counties. Many others, recorded in the nineteenth century, *ashen* 'ashes', *peasen* 'peas', *toen* 'toes', etc, have disappeared.

Kine 'cows' is of special interest as a 'double plural' (i.e. a plural formed twice over, like children's *mices* or *mens*) made by adding the *-n* of the *oxen* type to the old plural form *kye;* it has been found in recent times only in Cumbria and North Yorkshire, but the more regular old plural form *kye* has been found in the northern counties and also in Cheshire and Staffordshire.

Pronouns. A feature of most older dialect speech (though to a lesser extent in the east midlands and south-east) is the use of *thou, thee, thy, thine* and *thyself* for 'you, your, yours' and 'yourself': northern 'dis th' remember . . .?', 'thoo seems it' ('it suits you'), 'I'm glad to see thee', 'I kenned (knew) thy voice*', etc.

The forms of *-self* (in *myself, yourself,* etc) may appear in the singular as *sen, seln* and in the plural as *sen, seln* or *sens* in the north and midlands (*enjoying hissen, washing theirsens,* etc), all variant developments of ME *seluen;* and the simple personal pronoun *me, thee,* etc, is found for it in the north and west midlands and occasionally elsewhere — *wash me* 'wash myself', etc.

Demonstrative pronouns. In the north *yon, yond, yonder* are the most familiar demonstrative pronouns used to indicate an object 'over there', but *thir* 'these', *tho* 'those', *thon* 'that over there' and *thon ones* 'those over there' are perhaps less well known to southerners, likewise *thonder* 'yonder'. Perhaps these latter are combinations of *yon(d), yonder* and the pronouns which begin with *th.*

Prepositions and conjunctions. A dialect feature usually made much of is the use of the word *while* to mean 'until'. (A guide in York was recently heard to say to a group of foreigners 'All cross (the road) together and don't start to cross while I do'!) But this is not simply a northernism, although it is perhaps most common there; it is found also in the north midlands and east, and as far south as Berkshire. It was formerly much more widespread, being used, for example, by Shakespeare and Marlowe in this way.

Another item of interest here is *till* (ON *til*), which in north Cumbria (and occasionally elsewhere) can be used to mean 'to' ('till the doctor's', 'they gan ("go") till the kirk', 'quarter till twelve', etc).

Verbs. Apart from the fairly universal non-Standard -*s* ending in all present parts (*they keeps, we puts, I goes*, etc) the chief variations found in the north and in non-RSE speech generally are in the past tense and the past participle. In particular, we find numerous examples ending in -*ed* instead of having their usual form. *Knowed, growed, catched* and *seed* ('saw') are widespread, for example, and *comed* is also found in both north and south.

The verbs which in Anglo-Saxon times belonged to one particular conjugation show specially interesting archaic past tenses and past participles in present-day dialect: *give* has past tense singular *gav* in North Yorkshire, *get* has past participle *getten* and *gotten* in the north and north midlands; past tenses *spak* and *spok* are northern forms, as are also past participle forms *spok*, and *spak* (West Yorkshire), *spaken* (North Yorkshire).

Towns and cities

The area we have been discussing is mainly a rural one, apart from the great industrial complexes of Teesside and Tyneside. Towns like York, Richmond and Durham can be expected to share the major dialectal features of the surrounding countryside, except that these will perhaps be found in a less perfectly preserved state in the towns and there will be 'mixing' of types of speech. No doubt the locals will say they can distinguish the speech of a York man or a Richmond man or a Durham man from that of the countryside, but these distinctions are probably very local and minor ones to dialectologists, who are firstly concerned with mapping the most significant patterns.

The large cities, which have their own distinctive dialects, still await investigation, although an analysis has been made of pronunciation in Gateshead (W. Viereck, 1966), and a survey of Tyneside speech has been in progress from the University of Newcastle since 1963.

Meanwhile, on a lighter note, here, written in his own dialect, is what Mr J. Banks, a Sunderland man, sees as the difference between Sunderland and 'Geordie' (strictly the dialect of Tyneside). Sunderland people, he says, speak a dialect purely their own within a ten-mile radius:

'Dinnut think ave gorrout against being called a Geordie; av been proud ont in the past. But aa think wer should mak a distinction between the two, Geordies and Sunderlandonians.

The mair north yer come, the rougher the speech

seems tu be. But that's understandable in my eyes.
We live a rougher sort of life. Take the shipyards and
the pit: if yu dinnut speak the twang they think the's
sommat wrang wi yer . . .' (*Sunderland Echo*, 15th
February 1975)

The midlands and East Anglia

Pronunciation

We have already considered 'northern' pronunciations which
extend into the midland area, namely the short **a** sound in *grass*,
etc, and short **oo** in *cup*, etc, so we can begin with the knowledge
that these same features are present in at least the northern half of
that area.

If we now consider the other sounds mentioned under 'The
north', we find that, in words like *cow, brown, house*, we usually
hear a diphthong rather like the RSE sound, but sometimes in the
north midlands and further south this has become almost or
completely a long pure sound (a monophthong — *caa, braan,
haas*), not infrequently like a long version of the **a** in RSE *cat,
glad*, not far removed from the Cockney pronunciation of *Ta-ar
Bridge*.

In words of the *boot, fool, goose, spoon* class, where the north
has the **ia** (etc) sound, South and West Yorkshire people
traditionally have a sound **oo-i**, which is found nowhere else in
England, and can refer to the *schooil* and the *mooin*, and can
threaten 'Ah'll sooin fettle thi' ('I'll soon fix you'); people in south
Lancashire, Greater Manchester, Merseyside, north-west
Derbyshire, Cheshire and Staffordshire, however, tend to
pronounce this as a long **oo** but with the tongue very far forward in
the mouth, giving an impression of the *u* in French *tu, lune;* this is
also the case in East Anglia and we shall meet it again in the
south-west.

The *bone, loaf, road* class continues in the north midlands with
a sound **ooa** rather like the diphthong in RSE *doer* — sometimes
being replaced by an **aw** sound in imitation of RSE so that, for
example, dialectal *coke* and RSE *cork* sound similar. In the rest of
the midlands one hears either a diphthong something like the RSE
one or a long pure vowel made with lips rounded, rather like
French *eau*. It is generally regarded as a special East Anglian
characteristic that this sound becomes long **oo** and certainly a very
close sound of this type may be heard there, but there is a more
general dialectal tendency in the midlands and south for this to
happen.

In the related group of words *coal, coat, hole* and others South
and West Yorkshire and central Lancashire uniquely have **oi** and
dialect speakers here can speak about a *coil-'oil* 'coal-hole' (even a

fish-'oil 'fish and chip shop') and a *fur coit* 'fur coat'. Perhaps the most evocative word to exemplify this sound, however, is *thoil*, i.e. *thole* (OE *tholian*) 'suffer, endure', etc, as in 'I couldn't thoil t'brass' ('I couldn't afford the money').

In words like *eat, meat, steal* (usually spelled with *ea*, but this does not include all words with this spelling), we shall often hear in traditional dialect a sound like RSE **ay** in Lancashire, Greater Manchester, Merseyside, South and West Yorkshire, Cheshire, Staffordshire, north Derbyshire and north Nottinghamshire (as well as in some other parts of the country). There is a traditional Yorkshire put-off: 'Them as *ayts* mooast puddin' 'll get mooast *mayt*' — 'Those who eat most (Yorkshire) pudding will get most meat'. All these, together with words like *sheep, green, weeds*, etc, have an **ee** sound in RSE, have a very complicated historical development and can be heard with various sounds in the dialects — if not with **ee**, then with **é** or the *'ear'* sound described above or the **ay** sound just mentioned.

In a west-midland area defined by an arc extending as far north as the south Cumbrian border, as far south as south-west Gloucestershire, and to the east enclosing a western strip of West Yorkshire, the western half of Derbyshire, all of Staffordshire and a western strip of Warwickshire (enclosing most of West Midlands) and north-west Gloucestershire, we can hear an **o** sound in words like *hand, gander, man*, where the vowel is followed by an **n.** This is a feature already evidenced in medieval manuscripts from the same area.

In the northern half of a similar area, extending a little further to the east but not so far north, we find another old pronunciation: in words like *hang, ring, tongue*, a final **g** is pronounced, where it is not pronounced in RSE. This is a very enduring feature, which one can hear not only from older people but from younger and more educated people.

A note on East Anglia. East Anglia shares many of the characteristic features of the midlands generally (see above), but stands out for its 'sing-song' intonation patterns, the closeness of the sounds in the *bone, loaf, road* class (*boon, loof, rood*) and *boot, fool, goose, spoon* class (see above), its retention of initial **h** and the frequency of the glottal stop ('a bi' o' bre' n bu'er'); among the older generation **v** may still be heard as **w** in, e.g., *viper, vinegar, victuals* (locally *wittles*) — but, again, this is a more widespread feature, preserved in Cockney, for example, up to the last century. These features, combined with a certain drawling articulation and a very rich dialect vocabulary, mark out the area as one of great interest and distinctiveness.

Vocabulary

A number of Scandinavian words penetrate midland areas, mostly in the east. *Stee* 'ladder', already mentioned, is an example of one that is recorded in much of West and South Yorkshire and Humberside; *stithy* 'anvil' (ON *stethi*) is found throughout Lincolnshire as well as the north; *slape* 'slippery' (ON *sleipr*) extends to north Derbyshire, north Nottinghamshire and most of Lincolnshire, and *bairn* and *beck* have also been mentioned. We can also note, among others, *lad* 'son' or 'boy', *lass* 'daughter' or 'girl', which are found in the north midlands as well as the north; *teem* 'pour' (ON *toema*) is now used in RSE only in the expression 'teeming with rain' but can be used in dialect with reference to pouring out tea and other things: a clear boundary across the country from north Cheshire to the Wash separates northern and midland *teem* from *pour*, although the latter is found further north, where it is clearly gaining ground over its rival. *Clip* 'shear' (ON *klippa*) is likewise current down to a boundary stretching from central Lancashire to south Norfolk.

A selection of other old and well-established dialect words might include those for:

Autumn: *Back-end* is still the usual dialect expression throughout the north and midlands (excepting Lincolnshire), contrasting with *fall* (*of the leaf* or *year*) in the dialect-speaking rest of the country.

Fig. 2. Mucking the land with a Suffolk *tumbrel*.

19

Brew (tea): The firmly entrenched midland word is *mash*, giving way to the (possibly) Scandinavian-influenced *mask* or *mast* in the far north.

Farmcart: Here a cluster of East Anglian words are of special interest — Essex *tumble*, Suffolk and south Norfolk (also Salop) *tumbrel* (see fig. 2), Norfolk *tumbler*, all probably of French origin.

Gutter (of a house): *Launder* is a French word too (OF *lavendier*), perhaps adopted from mining use, and now found only in North Yorkshire, Derbyshire and Cornwall. Northern *spout* (MDu *spouten*) gives way to *spouting* in the midlands (also found in the north), with the peripheral words *trough/troughing* (OE *trog*) found in East Anglia and on the Welsh and Yorkshire/Lancashire borders.

Hay-loft: *Tallet*, a Welsh border (and south-western) word in various forms (*tollet*, *tallent*, *tollant*, *tollart*, *talfat*), is derived from Welsh *taflawd* (ultimately from Latin) and may have spread from Wales by the agency of travelling people such as casual harvest labourers or drovers in the medieval period and subsequently.

Hedgehog: *Urchin* (ONF *herichon*) occurs in the west midlands and Welsh border area and also in a long diagonal sweep from the far north-west to central Lincolnshire. These two areas were probably once a united one, now deeply eroded by native and RSE *hedgehog*.

Path (through a field): *Pad*, a word of Low German or Dutch origin, is entrenched in the midlands and is a specially interesting word, being first heard of (*OED*) in 1567, and stated to be in origin a word of vagabonds' cant, which seemingly got into dialect as the ordinary word for 'path'.

Splinter: Various words, mainly of medieval German or Dutch origin, occupy the midlands — *speel* (of Scandinavian origin) is found in south Lincolnshire (as well as in parts of the north), with *spile* (MDu, MLG *spille*, etc) in Greater Manchester and Merseyside and *spill* (of a similar origin) in a small central Welsh border area; *splint* (MDu *splinte*) holds the west midlands, *shiver* (early ME *scifer*) most of Lincolnshire and Norfolk, *sliver* (OE *·slifan* + *-er*) Suffolk, Essex and East Sussex, and RSE *splinter* (MDu *splinter*) the larger central and south-western areas of the country. *Speel* and *spill* are clearly related to the northern expressions *spelk* (OE *spelc*), *spell* and *spoal* (? ON *spolr*).

Grammar

The midlands have numerous grammatical characteristics different from both RSE and other forms of dialect.

Nouns with *-n* or *-en* endings are found occasionally: *flen* 'fleas' was recently recorded from Salop, Hereford and Worcester, and sometimes appears as *flens* in these counties. *Housen* 'houses', once apparently general in England except in the north, has been recently found among older people in two areas — one in Essex and East Anglia, and one in the west stretching from Hereford and Worcester through Gloucestershire to Oxfordshire and Berkshire, with occasional outliers.

Children is of special interest: the 'correct' form (historically speaking) is actually *childer*, which has developed quite regularly from ME *childre*, but an *-n* ending was added to some forms giving us present-day RSE *children*. *Childer* is, however, retained in dialect in the north midlands and occasionally in the south.

Map 4. Dialectal forms of *she* (after *SED*).

Pronouns. *Thou, thee, thy, thine* and *thyself* are used, though not in the eastern part of the area: except in the north of England, the forms *hisn, hern, ourn, yourn, theirn* are also widespread. The forms of the pronoun *she* (map 4), however, should be particularly noted: directly related to *she* itself is *shoo,* confined fairly closely to South and West Yorkshire. This may perhaps be a 'blend' or hybrid form of *she* and north-west midland *hoo* (OE *hēo*); such hybrids tend to arise when an area of one form abuts on to an area of another. Finally, *her* is characteristic of the central and southern west midlands and the south-western peninsula (except for west Cornwall).

In the old area of the West Riding of Yorkshire *us* can be heard for 'our' ('one on uz own', etc), and also in east Cheshire, north Derbyshire and north Staffordshire, and *we* 'our' has also been recorded in south Staffordshire. The use of these personal pronouns in possessive situations was once very much more common in dialect, and one could apparently use *we, us, thee, ye, you* and *he* for 'our', 'thine', 'your' and 'his' in different parts of England.

The pronoun *its* did not exist in medieval English and was, so to speak, invented — apparently in the south of England — towards the end of the sixteenth century, supplanting earlier and especially west-midland *hit* or *it*. (Shakespeare's Fool in *King Lear* says: 'For, you know, Nuncle/The hedge-sparrow fed the cuckoo so long/ That it had it head bit off by it young.') In the north midlands this old form *hit,* or *it* as it is now, is still used, i.e. in Lancashire, Greater Manchester, South and West Yorkshire, Humberside, north Derbyshire, east Cheshire, north Staffordshire and north Lincolnshire.

In addition to expressions like *wash me* 'wash myself', northern, midland and other dialects also use a pronoun where it is unnecessary in RSE — *sit thysen down, lie yourself down,* and even (in Lancashire and Derbyshire) *play them, play themselves.*

Conjunctions and prepositions of interest in the midlands include, as above, the well-known use of *while* for 'till' and that of *without* for 'unless' (throughout the west midlands and in Yorkshire, Humberside, central Lancashire, north Lincolnshire and north-east Leicestershire and also in some scattered southern areas).

Verbs. The present plural ending of verbs used to end in *-ath* or *-eth* in earlier times but has disappeared in modern RSE — *we come, you see, they have,* etc. A small area of the west midlands (mainly Derbyshire, Cheshire and Staffordshire), however, adds the ending *-n* or *-en* — already present in medieval times in this area — *we putten* 'we put', *han you . . . ?* 'have you . . . ?', etc. The strange-sounding *I bin* 'I am' — i.e. the usual western dialect form *I be* plus *-n* ending (see map 5) — also occurs in Salop and its

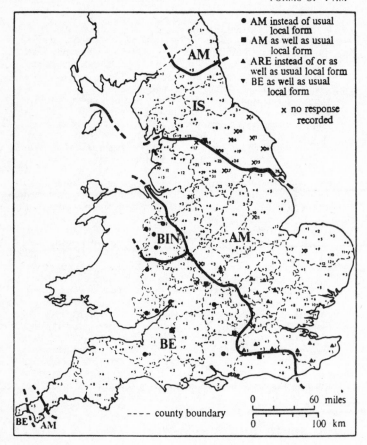

Map 5. Forms of *I am* (after *SED*). Note several important dialect areas: (1) a line roughly parallel with Watling Street divides *I am* from *I be;* (2) the Humber marks the southern limit of *I is* (ON *ek es*); (3) *I bin* (= *be* + *-n* ending) emerges as a sub-area of *I be;* (4) a small area of *I am* in west Cornwall represents the adoption of an early form of RSE here.

environs.

In the present participle (*I am going, they are sitting,* etc) an *a-* is prefixed in scattered places in the midlands, both east and west, as far north as Cheshire and as far west as Wiltshire and Gloucestershire (it is missing in Essex, Surrey, Kent, Sussex and Hampshire): 'I ain't a-going home yet', etc. This is a relic of the OE *on* which preceded the verbal noun.

Again, *-ed* forms are frequent in past tenses and past participles — *knowed, growed, weared,* etc, just as in the north. This is a common dialect feature, especially in these particular verbs.

And again, we find archaic forms in some verbs — past participles *getten* and *gotten* (still used in America) as in the north, biblical past tense *spake* (except in the eastern part of the midlands).

For *reach* the forms *roach* (past tense) and *roached* (past participle) are recorded in southern Northamptonshire, this verb having been re-formed on the model of *write-wrote, ride-rode,* etc.

Towns and cities

The mixed dialects of midland towns still await investigation. There are old glossaries of Sheffield dialect (EDS 57 and 62, 1888) and Leeds dialect (C. Clough Robinson, London — John Russell Smith — 1862), and people have written on the specialised dialects of cutlering and the steel industry (see *Transactions of the Yorkshire Dialect Society*). But published accounts of the dialects of Sheffield and Leeds as a whole — as well as those of Manchester, Liverpool, Nottingham, Leicester, Birmingham, Derby, Stafford, Peterborough, Northampton, Corby, Luton, Bedford — we still do not have. Dr Peter Wright, of the University of Salford, is engaged on city dialects and is expected to publish a book on these shortly. North Staffordshire speech has been studied in the University of Keele extra-mural department (see *Journal of the Lancashire Dialect Society,* 19, 1970).

The south and south-west

Pronunciation

Let us now look at the pronunciations we have traced down the country from the north, adding one or two others which are specially characteristic of the south of England.

The sound heard in *cow, brown, house* is, again, usually a diphthong, except in popular London speech, where once again we can hear that simple, pure sound without any glide — *kaa* 'cow', *braan* 'brown', *'aas* 'house' (not the sound in RSE *grass* or *car,* but further forward in the mouth).

A completely different and unique development has taken place in Devon, east Cornwall and west Somerset (see map 6), where the whole diphthong is pronounced with the lips rounded, the first part of it rather like the sound in French *peu*, the second like that in French *tu*. West Cornwall escapes this development because the type of English which came to be spoken there as Cornish was given up is thought to have been of a more 'standard' variety than that found in Devon and Somerset.

This also applies, in particular, to the very 'fronted' sound (as in French *tu* again) found in this area in *boot, food, moon, spoon, good, took, cook,* etc. We have already seen this 'fronting' (i.e. pronounced right at the front of the mouth) in west-midland counties and East Anglia, but it is more emphatic here in the south-west and quite unmistakable. Elsewhere in the south the sound is reasonably close to RSE. Attempts to find Celtic sources for these south-western phenomena (which mark off Devon, east Cornwall and west Somerset as a separate dialect area and are probably post-medieval developments) should be regarded with scepticism.

The *bone, loaf, road* and *coal, coat, hole* classes in the south

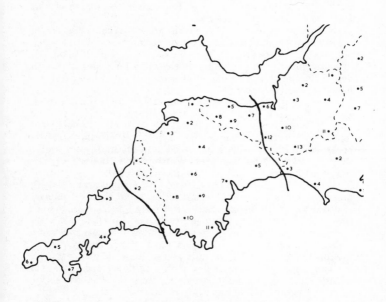

Map 6. The south-western 'rounded vowel' area (after **SED**).

remain recognisably close to RSE pronunciation — except that sometimes one can hear a long púre sound like that in French *eau* (or even closer) instead of the usual diphthong — and in the south-east, especially the London area, this becomes more like the sound heard in RSE *brown, cow, house*.

In words of the *eat, meat, steal* and *beat, leave, reach* classes (which differed from each other in their vowels in some Middle English dialects), older people in the south, as elsewhere, frequently use a pronunciation like RSE **ay** or French **é** — 'a good cup tay' ('a good cup of tea').

The vowel sound in *cat, lack, sad, stand*, etc, varies somewhat in the south from area to area. Over the greater part of England it is more or less like RSE **a,** but in two areas, namely parts of the south-west (the southern Welsh border and parts of Somerset and Avon) and the whole of the south-east, the sound is pronounced with the tongue slightly higher in the mouth, i.e. nearer to the RSE **e** position. In the London area and the Home Counties it does frequently attain to **e**.

In the south — including popular London speech — **o** before **f, s** and **th** is still an **aw** sound (*awff, crawss, clawth* 'off, cross, cloth'); this is now obsolete in RSE except in the speech of old-fashioned, conservative speakers.

A very important matter which arises in connection with southern and western dialects is that of the pronunciation of **r**. Not only are there more varieties than the one we hear in RSE, but **r** is also sometimes pronounced before consonants (e.g. in *cart, horse*) and at the end of words (e.g. in *hear, nor*) whereas in RSE it has been lost in those positions.

Firstly, then, the different varieties. 'Ordinary' **r** (as in *rabbit, mirage, hear it*) is found all over the main area of England. The other varieties are more peripheral. We have already noted the 'burr' in Northumberland and Tyne and Wear, and we occasionally find a 'trilled' or 'rolled' **r** in the north too. In the south-west (including Somerset, Wiltshire and Hampshire), **r** is 'reverted' or 'retroflex', i.e. it is pronounced with the tongue curled back further in the mouth than usual. In a small area of south Somerset this can be heard 'aspirated', i.e. as **hr.** In west Somerset and north-east Devon the **r** and a following **i** or **e** are sometimes reversed, so that one can hear *erd* (with the **r** pronounced) 'red', and even *herd* 'red', as well as the more familiar and more widespread (much of the south) *gurt* 'great', *purdy* 'pretty'.

Pronounced before consonants and at the ends of words, **r** is found — especially among older, more traditional speakers — in a large south-western area stretching from East Sussex as far north as Cheshire and occurs again in Lancashire and the Pennine area. In Northumberland and Tyne and Wear the 'burr' can also be heard before consonants and at the ends of words.

We now have to consider one or two other consonant sounds in the south. Perhaps the best-known of these is the pronunciation at the beginning of words of **f**, **s**, **th** and **sh** as **v**, **z**, **dh** (as in RSE *then*) and **zh** (as in RSE *measure*), e.g. *varmer, zeed* ('saw'), *dhatch, zhilling*. This has long been familiar from stage dialect, but in reality it is now a very recessive feature, which, in medieval times widespread as far north as the Watling Street, is now found most consistently in Devon and the neighbouring counties, as well as Wiltshire and east Hampshire, although in some words (especially those beginning with **f**) occurring as far north as Gloucestershire and west Hereford and as far east as the western borders of Surrey and Hampshire. Outside this area examples are few and far between, though an odd one can apparently still be heard in East Sussex and the rural south-east. West Cornwall has fewer examples, once again because of its adoption not of south-western dialect but of a 'standard' type of English. When followed by **r** (e.g. in *three, through*), **th** in the south-west may be heard as **d**, so that we get *dree, drew*, etc. These sound-changes are evidenced historically in numerous place-names, such as Verwood (Dorset) 'fair wood', Venn (Cornwall) 'fenn', Vange (Essex) 'marshy district' (OE *fenn* + · *gē* 'district'), South Zeal (Devon) 'south hall' (OE *sele*), Zennor (Cornwall) 'St Senara', Druckham (Cornwall) — *Throcombe* in the fourteenth century.

In popular London pronunciation the simplification of **th** to f (*fank* 'thank', *moff* 'moth') and of **dh** to **v** (*ven* 'then', *gavver* 'gather') is well-known and indeed occurs further afield — in the Home Counties and even in the north. There is, however, an important group of words — *that, the, their, then, there, these, those*, etc — in which RSE **dh** is **d** in London dialect and the south-east, although younger people often produce a cross between **d** and **dh** instead of a fully formed **d**.

Finally, we must mention loss and addition of **w** and **y**, mainly in the south-west and west. At the beginning of words **w** may be lost before **oo** but added at the beginning of a word or inserted after a consonant before certain vowels. Thus, as far north as Salop and as far east as West Sussex (but not in west Devon and Cornwall) we can hear *'oman* 'woman' and *'ool* 'wool', but — more sporadically now — *wold* 'old', *bwoiling* 'boiling', *lwonely* 'lonely', *pwoison* 'poison', etc.

Loss of **y** in, e.g., *yeast, yes, yesterday, year* is much the same, except that we also find it lost in parts of eastern England (Lincolnshire, Suffolk). The addition of **y** is sporadically found — mainly in the south-west — in, e.g., *earn, earth* (thus *yearn, yearth*).

Vocabulary

We may now turn to examine a selection of southern dialect vocabulary.

Ant: *Emmet* — a word deriving from the same root as *ant* itself (OE *æmete*) — is the regular dialect word throughout the southern counties. A similar example is 'newt', which has a dialectal parallel *eft, evet, ewt, ebbet,* etc, throughout the southern counties, derived, like *newt,* from OE *efeta.*

Brew (tea): The two old southern dialect words are *wet* and *soak,* the latter only in Cornwall and west Devon, but the standard word *brew* is also found everywhere.

Farmyard: *Court* (a French word) or *back-court* is found in Wiltshire, Devon, east Cornwall and west Hampshire, alternating here with the native expression *barton* (OE *bere-tūn*).

Field: *Ground* (OE *grund*) survives in parts of the central south-west.

Mole: *Wont* (OE *wont*) occurs in the Welsh border counties and the south-west as far as west Hampshire.

Pigsty: West Somerset and east Devon have *lewze* (OE *hlōse*) for this item, but further down the south-western peninsula, in Cornwall, we find *pig's crow,* which, together with some more northerly counterparts, namely *pig-cree* and *pig-crew,* also *hen-cree, -crew, crewyard,* etc, derives ultimately from Celtic sources.

Retch: The south-western word for this idea is the expressive *urge* (perhaps a form of *retch*), but further north we find *heave* and *retch.* Interestingly *reave,* near the central Lancashire coast and in central Gloucestershire, may be a blend of *heave* and *retch.*

Scarecrow: Northern *flay-crow* (the first part perhaps from ON *fleyja* 'to scare, terrify'), midland *mawkin,* and various others give way in the south to *mommet* (OF *mahumet*), *gally-bagger* (OE *ā-gælwan* 'to alarm' + ?), and, in Cornwall, *bucca* (Corn. *bucca* 'hobgoblin', 'scarecrow').

One easily identifiable group of words in the south-west is those of Cornish origin. These, mainly the names of things, are chiefly restricted to the area west of Truro, where Cornish was last spoken, but some have been found further east. In addition to *pig's crow* and *bucca,* cited above, we may mention the following: *bannal* 'a broom' (Corn. *banal* 'broom flower or plant', 'besom'; cf. place-names Benallack, Carvannel, etc); *clunk* 'to swallow' and *clunker* 'windpipe' (probably Corn. *collenky* 'to swallow down'); *dram* 'swath' (Corn. *dram*); *fuggan* 'pastry dinner-cake' (Corn. *fūgen*); *gook* 'bonnet' (Corn. *cūgh* 'head-covering', etc, see fig. 3); *griglans* 'heather' (Corn. *grüglon;* cf. the place-name Gregland); *groushans* 'dregs' (Corn. *growjyon*); *hoggan* 'pastry-cake' (Corn. *hogen*); *kewny* 'rancid' (Corn. *kewnyek* 'mossy, mouldy, hoary'); *muryan* 'ant' (Corn. *muryon;* obscurely related to the second element in northern *pissy-moors, -moos, -mowers, -mires,* etc); *rab* 'gravel' (cf. Corn. *rabmen* 'granite gravel' and place-name Rabman Zawn); *scaw* 'elder-tree' (Corn. *scaw;* cf. place-names Trescowe, Nanscow, Nanscawn, etc); *stank* 'to walk, trample, step' (on, in) (Corn. *stankya*); *whidden* 'weakling' (of a litter of pigs; Corn. *gwyn*, later *gwidden* 'white').

Some of these Cornish 'loan-words' are not ultimately Cornish, but Latin, French or English, and have come into English *via* Cornish. From a very early period Cornish was susceptible to foreign influences to a remarkable degree, and its medieval and later literature is full of words and phrases from all three languages. Examples are:

Bulhorn 'snail' (Corn. *bulhorn*, a late Corn. word, adapted from an English dialectal nickname for the snail); *bussa* 'salting-trough', 'bread-bin' (probably ME *busse*, OF *buce, busse* 'barrel' and medieval Latin *bussa*); *croust* 'snack' (Corn. *crowst*, OF *crouste*, Latin *crusta*); *flam-new* 'brand-new' (*flam-* from Corn. *flam* 'flame', from Latin *flamma*); *geek* 'gape' (Corn. *gȳky* 'to

WEST PENWITH

NORTH CORNWALL

CAMBORNE (DOLCOATH)

ST. AGNES & SCORRIER

Fig. 3. Examples of the Cornish *gook*.

peep', perhaps from English *keek*); *hoggan* 'haw' (Corn. *hogan*, probably from OE **hagga* 'haw'); *peeth* 'well' (Corn. *pȳth*; cf. Latin *puteus*).

There may be, and there certainly once were, further Cornish words in the English dialect of west Cornwall, whether ultimately of Cornish or some other origin. But attempts to find Cornish words in Devon and elsewhere and attempts to find Celtic etymologies for everything in English dialect should be regarded with scepticism.

Grammar

Grammatically the southern area is one of conservatism (as compared with the north as an area of innovation), and it is here, especially in areas remote from London and the Home Counties, that we may expect to find the most ancient features of traditional English usage. Some of these, like south-western *utch* 'I' (ME *ich*), up to the last century found in Somerset, have now disappeared (*us* in south Somerset may, however, be a relic of this), but others — *thou, thee, thy*, etc — linger on.

Nouns. Having said this, it is odd that few traces of the old plural of nouns in *-n* or *-en* are to be found here, although the 'triple' plurals *hipsens* 'hips' (*hips* + *-en* + *-s*) and *hawsens* 'haws' (*haws* + *-en* + *-s*) have been found in south Oxfordshire and central Gloucestershire respectively. The regular old plural *chicken* (for RSE 'chickens', a double plural), OE *cicen*, plural *cicenu* (note, no *-s*), is found in the south-western counties and sporadically in the western and south-eastern counties (and, very sparingly, in Lancashire).

Pronouns. We have already mentioned the disappearance of *utch;* one ancient survival throughout the south-west, however, is *'n* 'him', 'it' — 'I seed ("saw") 'n', 'put 'n outside', etc — which is derived from the OE pronoun *hine* 'him' (pronounced hi-neh), lost to RSE, because replaced by the dative form *him* in early times.

In the south, more than anywhere else, we find the pronouns exchanging their functions, e.g. *she* (subject) being used for *her* (object) and *her* for *she*, but there usually seems to be a restriction on this process in that the objective form is used for the subject only when the pronoun is being used in unemphatic situations (e.g. *didn't her?* '. . . didn't she?'), and, contrariwise, the subject form is used only as the emphatic form of the object (e.g. *I told she*). In the south-west, then, we find *I* used for 'me', *we* for 'us' (this also embraces all the south except for Surrey, Kent and the south-east), *he* for 'him', *she* for 'her' (less common), and *they* for 'them'; contrariwise *us* for 'we' (spreading into the south midlands), *him* and *'n* for 'he', *them* for 'they' (spreading into the west midlands).

In east Cornwall the strange-sounding pronoun *mun* 'them' (*be mun . . . ?* 'are they . . . ?', etc) occurs — it was current in

Somerset, Devon and Cornwall in the nineteenth century; its origin and history are obscure.

Thou, thee, thy, etc, are, of course, used in the south (except in the eastern part), as is also *ye,* usually current as *'ee.*

Demonstrative pronouns. These show some interesting forms here, especially the well-known *thick* (the *th* pronounced as in RSE *this*), *thicky* 'this', *thuck, thucker* 'that' (all from ME *thilke*), and *theseum* 'these'. *They* ('those') — 'in they days', etc — is also in frequent use.

Adjectives. We have not so far had cause to mention adjectives, since in the north and midlands these are very much the same as in RSE. In the south, however, we meet an interesting deviation. In RSE many adjectives denoting material end in *-en,* e.g. *wooden, golden* (and cf. the archaic 'in the olden days'), and this is extended further in the south-west, so that a farmer shears his sheep 'down on the *boarden* floor' (of the barn), a child eats his sweets out of a *papern* bag, and cake that is not home-made is necessarily *boughten* cake.

Verbs. The *to* which occurs before a verb has a widespread dialect parallel form *for to* (as the song has it, 'I want for to go to Widecombe Fair'), and in the south the *to* often completely disappears, leaving us with, e.g., 'I came for see the doctor', 'you've got for know how to do it'.

One or two examples of the extremely ancient and rare third singular *-eth* ending remain in east Cornwall and south Devon. This derives from Old English but began to be supplanted by *-es* in Middle English, although the old *-eth* forms were retained as late as the seventeenth century, e.g. in the Authorised Version of the Bible (1611). The ending is rare now, but *her wear'th* 'she wears' and *her'th returned* 'she's returned' have been recorded in recent times in east Cornwall, and *dooth* 'does' (also *I'th seen*) from south Devon.

Sometimes the *-eth* ending was lost in Middle English *without* being replaced by *-es,* thus giving a form with no ending. Such forms are fairly frequent in the present-day southern dialects, especially in the south-west and East Anglia, where we can find, for example, *she wear, it hurt* (present tense).

The infinitive form (modern English *come, ride, see,* etc) of some verbs ended in *-ian* in Old English (*gaderian* 'gather', *nerian* 'save', etc), and there seems to be a relic of the *-i-* of this form left in some south-western verbs; thus, for example, (north Devon) 'There isn't many (who) can sheary ("shear") now'. The *-y* ending, however, is probably added to verbs indiscriminately now, as in the Cornish proverb 'They that can't schemy (i.e. use their brain) must lowster' (i.e. do labouring work).

In RSE *do* is only used with the infinitive in certain situations: questions — 'Do you see?', emphasis — 'I do want to', negation —

'I don't know'. But in the south-west it is often used with the infinitive in contexts such as 'I d'go every day', 'as far as I d'know', 'He d'come here on Tuesdays'. This occurs in an area round the river Severn comprising places in south-west Hereford, Gloucestershire and Avon, in another very small area in central and west Cornwall, and in a third, larger area comprising parts of Wiltshire, Dorset and environs. But these were all probably once part of a large connected area.

Again here the present participle is found prefixed by *a-:* 'There she was, *a-going* down the road . . .' Further, the past participle was sometimes prefixed by *ge-* in Old English (ME *y-, i-*), and traces of this too remain in the south-west as *a-* in, e.g., *a-found, a-put, a-done, a-broked* ('broken').

The *-ed* forms of past tenses and past participles continue in the south, e.g. *borned* 'born' (recorded from west Cornwall; = past participle *born* + *-ed* ending); *wored* 'worn' (south Somerset, Cornwall); *wored* 'wore' (west Somerset); *woreded* 'worn' (central Devon); *stoled* 'stole, stolen' (south-west); *doed* 'done' (south-west).

Strange and archaic forms in some of the verbs, due to past changes in the language, are again to be found in the south, e.g. *gov* 'gave, given' (recorded from west Cornwall), *sot* 'sat' (west Somerset, central and south Devon), *spok* 'spoken' (south-west), *spake* 'spoke' (north-west Surrey).

Towns and cities

In the south we do not find the large industrial towns of the midlands, but we do have to take into account the influence of popular London dialect, with its characteristic sounds: roughly **a** (*cab, matter*) tending towards **e; o** in *off, cough,* etc tending towards **aw; uh** (*butter, mother*) towards **a; ay** (*gate, change*) towards long **i** (RSE *fine,* etc); long **i** (*line, type*) towards **oi;** the sound in *no* towards that in *now;* **th** in *this, there,* etc becoming **d;** frequent use of the glottal stop (*bu'er, wa'er*); **l** becoming 'vocalised' to **oo** in, e.g., *bull, field* (roughly *boo, fiood*). Many of these are also characteristic of Cockney proper, from which, however, we may add **ow** becoming an **ah** type of sound (*tahn, 'ahs*), **f** for **th** in, e.g., *think, thirty,* and perhaps **aw** for **ah** in *heart, last,* etc.

First of all, as London has spread its suburbs further and further out into the countryside of the Home Counties, so its dialect has gone with it — with pre-war suburban settlers, wartime refugees and others who left London for what was then countryside and have stayed since. As this sprawl has eaten up the country villages, so its suburban tongue has gradually obliterated the old country speech in counties like Kent, Surrey and Sussex, once the homes of traditional English dialect as much as Devon and Yorkshire still are. And a contributory factor to this loss of dialect is no doubt the replacement of native villagers by commuters.

Furthermore, this popular London dialect has pushed its way to the south and east coasts and up as far as Norwich (which may account for Jonathan Mardle's judgement, in his *Broad Norfolk*, that Norwich 'has developed a slipshod urban argot that is different from, and inferior to, old-fashioned Norfolk . . . an adenoidal gabble, which schoolmasters justly deplore'!). The constant bombardment of the south-eastern holiday resorts by Londoners may be partly responsible for this, as may also commuting. But whatever the causes, the traditional features of many of these dialects (e.g. the 'retroflex' r formerly heard in words like *carter* and the v, z, etc, in words like *field* and *son*) have all but disappeared and are absent in the speech of younger people, except perhaps in the far reaches of the countryside. The old dialects of the south-east are thus undergoing a complete change.

3. Occupational and specialised vocabularies

The distinctive features of the special dialects of farmers, railway workers, fishermen, actors, civil servants and so on are found mainly in their vocabularies, although the members of these groups will also, in general, use the sounds and grammar of their own social class, and — if they have a regional dialect — also of their geographical region. (However, there are also special 'voices' associated with some professions — we can all recognise that of a sergeant major on parade, and sometimes, perhaps, a clergyman in his pulpit.) Here, then, we shall exemplify what makes, say, miners or steelworkers linguistically distinct as a group, namely the words they use in the industry or in contexts closely associated with it, and consider how these terms differ from place to place up and down the country in the same occupation. Naturally, we cannot give examples from every industry but shall deal with one or two of those which have been investigated.

Farming

Many farming words have already been mentioned within the regional plan we adopted, and here we can exemplify specialised aspects of farming by looking at one further group of words. This group relates to haymaking in the Yorkshire Dales, which is really three processes, mowing, haymaking proper and *leading*.

(1) Mowing machines were not introduced into the Dales until the second half of the nineteenth century, but hand-mowing with a *lea* (scythe) is only remembered by the very elderly now. Before

hay-time, mowers selected their own pole and the *lea* was then set up by the blacksmith, consisting of *shaft* (pole), blade, nibs (upper and lower), heel hoop, wedges and grass-nail. Attached to the top end of the *shaft* was a wooden *strickle* for whetting.

(2) Once scythed, the grass was submitted to a process of *strawing* or *shaking out*, turning, drying in small heaps called *foot-cocks*, larger ones called *jockeys* or even larger ones called *pikes*. *Strawing* by hand was the most approved way: up to about sixty years ago *straw-girls* or *straw-boys*, about four to one mower, followed the scythemen across the field and *strawed* the grass by bending low and tossing it alternately with each hand over the opposite shoulder. But the frequently employed Irishmen, using forks, could *straw* or *scale* two rows at a time of the hand-mown *swiaths* (swathes). When built, the haycocks were protected from the wind by a hay-rope thrown over them, made with the help of a *thraw-crook* or a rake.

(3) *Leading*, or carrying the dry hay to the *lathe* (barn), was done by *sweeping* it with a *hay-sweep* (a gate-like wooden frame) or piling it on to a sledge, pulled by a horse or perhaps two. When using a sledge, two men at each side gathered together *kemmings* ('combings' — i.e. armfuls) of hay with their rakes and placed them on in layers. The whole was then secured by a rope.

Loads were tipped off sideways; the *forker-up* then tossed the hay with a fork through a hole into the *mewstead* or *up on t'baulks* (loft over the cow-stalls) where it was spread evenly and trodden well down. Finally, *knag-* or *drag-rakes* were pulled by hand up and down the meadows to collect hay that had been missed.

Layers of hay cut with the hay-knife or hay-*spiad* (-spade) from the hay in the *mewstead* were called *desses* (*canches* in Swaledale).

Haymaking was an exhausting process and the workers no doubt richly deserved their break or *bait*, *drinking(s)*, or *ten-o-clocks*, and also the supper or *mell* which marked the end of this annual procedure.

The technical terms which have emerged here are local to one comparatively small region: farmers in Devon or Wiltshire would use a quite different set. Our next example shows how such technical terms vary from area to area round the country.

Fishing

Fishing is another traditional British occupation, but both this and mining are less stable than farming, and there has been (and still is) much movement of workers between areas. This results in the transference of words from one part of the country to another, and thus they become geographically widespread within the industries concerned.

Two surveys of fishing terms have been carried out, one by Dr Peter Wright, of the University of Salford (see the *Journal of the*

Lancashire Dialect Society 16-17, 1967-8), and one by Dr W. Elmer, of Basel, and the selection below is taken from these surveys.

The types of the old local boats — the number of which is now considerably diminished — provide a rich variety of local names: the widely distributed *smack* is an example of a term which still survives even though the type it once described has changed or disappeared; the south-western *gig*, on the other hand, illustrates how old names are transferred to new boats of different structure (they are now motor-powered). From the north-east coast come *cobles* (*yawls* on Holy Island), while in East Anglia we find *alongshore boats, crab-boats* and *toshers; beach-boats* and *luggers* are found in the south-east, and in Cornwall and Devon *crab-boats* and (again) *toshers;* the north-west has *nobbies* among others; *punts* are found in East Anglia, the south-east and the north-west.

The various parts of the boats also produce local terms. Here once again there are differences in structure: there are, for example, three types of fulcrum in the boats, namely *rowlocks*, turning on a pin (universal); *tholes* or *tholepins*, vertical wooden pegs between which the oar works (almost as widespread); and *oar-ports*, a Scandinavian feature now found only in the crabbers of Cromer, Sheringham and Mundesley, which consist of two to three holes in the top plank called *orruck-holes* (from ME *orloc*, which is also the basis of *rowlock*).

Crab and lobster pots are also of different types — three main ones are used around the English and Welsh coasts: the south and south-west is the home of the *Cornish pot;* on the east and south-east coasts are found the *creel* or *creeve;* the recently introduced *barrel* type or *Frenchman's pot* is apparently gaining ground along the south coast.

One can still see part-time fishermen shrimping with a *pushnet* and a shrimp-basket in shallow waters, and this basket may be known as a *bushel-* (north Norfolk), *butter-* (Sussex) or *keep-basket* (west Cornwall), a *creel* (east and north coasts), a *skep* (Suffolk), a *swill* (Lancashire), among others.

The fish themselves have a great variety of names. The starfish has so many local names that it is hard to select. *Five-finger(s)* is found everywhere except the far north, with variants *fivelegs, fivefeet, fivetoes* occurring much less regularly. *Thorns* is a north-eastern term, as is also *frawns; hornheads* is found in north Norfolk, *cross-fish, cross-ones* in Lancashire and Cheshire.

A glance at even this minute selection of words shows some differences in the distribution of items. Some are widely accepted all round the coasts, e.g. *rowlocks*, also *braiding* (OE *bregdan*) 'net-making, -mending', and are thus trade jargon rather than regional dialect. Others are restricted to specific areas, like (mainly) north-western *web* 'oar-blade' and a south-western group *nozzle, nozzling, orsle* 'snood' (the thin line by means of which the hook is attached to the main line in 'long-lining', a type of winter fishing). Finally, some occur at widely separated places, indicative of the fishermen's movement from one place to another, e.g. *beeting* (OE *bētan*) 'net-making, -mending', found in Cleveland, North Yorkshire and Humberside, East Anglia, Kent and Sussex and the far west of Cornwall; *black-jack* 'coal-fish', found on the north-east coast, Suffolk, Essex, Kent, south Devon, Swansea and Cumbria; *shuttle* 'short stick for braiding', found in a cluster of north-eastern localities and in isolated instances in north Norfolk and West Sussex.

Mining

In mining, as in fishing, there have been frequent and large-scale movements of workers from one place to another, e.g. the large migrations which recently took place from County Durham to the Yorkshire-Derbyshire-Nottinghamshire coalfield and from the Forest of Dean to South Wales. Presumably reflecting this mobility, the keynotes of a recent investigation, again by Dr Peter Wright, are, on the one hand, variety — variety of words for one single notion within a small area — and, on the other, the widespread distribution of some words. Taking the second aspect first, a miner's working-place, for example, is known as *stall* in several midland coalfields and also in Gloucestershire, a water channel as *garland* in both North Wales and Somerset. Examples of the first aspect are: for 'stint' (i.e. the amount of work allotted to one miner), *stint, pog* and *sneck* from pits in the old West Riding of Yorkshire within a ten-mile radius of each other; for 'stallman' at Warsop (Nottinghamshire), *chargeman, stallman* and *butty*. In the Somerset pit, vertical wooden props are apparently *posts* if under three feet, *timber* if longer; *uprights* was given by an informant's friend during the survey, and they appear in broader dialect as *stimples* — in other words, four terms for a single basic idea.

A further small selection of terms from coalfields in different counties from Dr Wright's survey might include:

Miner: *Miner* itself (perhaps mainly southern), *collier* (perhaps mainly northern), and *pitman* in places as far apart as Tyne and Wear and Kent.

Pit-head: Sometimes *pit-top* is used for this, and we also find *bank* in Tyne and Wear, in South Yorkshire *pit-top* together with older *pit-bank* and technical *heap-stead*, and in Greater Manchester *heap-stead* and more modern *pit-brow*.

Haulage road: *Jig* (Salop), *rope road* (Nottinghamshire), *ginny* (South Yorkshire and Gloucestershire), *incline* (Somerset), *steep* (Kent), *spinney-brow* (Greater Manchester).

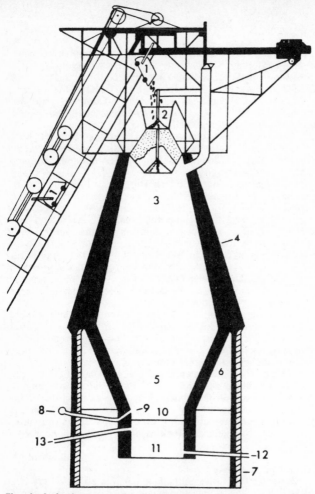

Fig. 4. A further example of industrial vocabulary: diagram of a Sheffield blast-furnace with parts labelled. 1 *skip* (small wheeled container to charge the furnace); 2 *hopper* (container for receiving the ore and passing it into the furnace); 3 *throat;* 4 *stack* ('chimney'); 5 *belly* (widest part of stack); 6 *bosh* (container round the belly); 7 *mantle* (to support the stack); 8 *bustle pipe* (distributing hot blast); 9 *tuyeres* (nozzles through which the air enters the furnace); 10 *hearth;* 11 *bottom;* 12 *slag-hole* or *slag-notch* (the place where the cinders, etc, come out); 13 *tap-hole* (small opening through which the metal is run out).

Deputy: In addition to *deputy* itself, there are *examiner* (Somerset) and *doggy* (Greater Manchester, South Yorkshire).

Depression in roof: *Slip* (West Yorkshire, Nottinghamshire), *pot-hole* (South Yorkshire, Nottinghamshire, Greater Manchester), *stone* (Tyne and Wear), *bad stone* (north Cumbria), *bad hole* (Nottinghamshire), *bad ground* (Salop), *bell* and *welver* (Gloucestershire), *bell-mould* (Somerset).

Brake on a tub: *Cow* (Tyne and Wear), *lashing-chain, clam-key* and *drag* (South Yorkshire), *clivvy* (Nottinghamshire), *lounge* (Somerset), *sprag* (Gloucestershire), *locker* (Salop), *coupling* (Greater Manchester).

An investigation of north Staffordshire terms meaning 'late for work' has been directed by Mr J. Levitt (see *Journal of the Lancashire Dialect Society* 19, 1970), the most common word being *franked*, used throughout the area, and the second most common *buzzed* (with obvious allusion to the buzzer being sounded), also in use in Cannock (south Staffordshire). To the north of Stoke-on-Trent, in Biddulph, Norton and Smallthorne, the word *sornet* (? = 'sounded') is in use; and in the village of Audley and in Tunstall, *in Dicky's meadow* has been reported ('Wey shall av't hurry up, or wey sal bey in Dicky's meadow', i.e. in 'queer street', i.e. late).

Overlain 'overslept' is the main reason for being late at work, but at Froghall in the Churnet valley the word *flung* occurs, which means 'made late': 'I was flung this morning and got franked'.

This scrutiny of a small area suggests that a nationwide survey of such terms would be exceptionally interesting.

A wealth of vocabulary clearly remains to be harvested not only from heavy industry but from such country crafts as charcoal-burning, basket-, hurdle-, hoop- and rake-making, coopering, smithing, thatching, brick-making, potting, wool-working, tanning, boot-making, and many more too numerous to mention (see especially the books by Jenkins and Hartley under Further Reading).

Bird and plant names

Local names for birds, animals and plants are a far cry from industrial language. Some domestic animal names have already

Map 7. Local names of the lapwing in Britain. Key: 1 *teeick* or *teeack;* 2 *teuchet;* 3 *peewit* and *peesweep;* 4 *tewit;* 5 *teäfit* or *teufit;* 6 *peewit* (a) *peewit* plus *plover,* (b) *peewit* plus *plover,* also *piewipe,* (c) *peewit* plus *plover,* also *horniwink;* 7 *green plover* (the broken line indicates that this can also be heard in south-west Scotland and certain of the Isles); •*lapwing* used popularly.

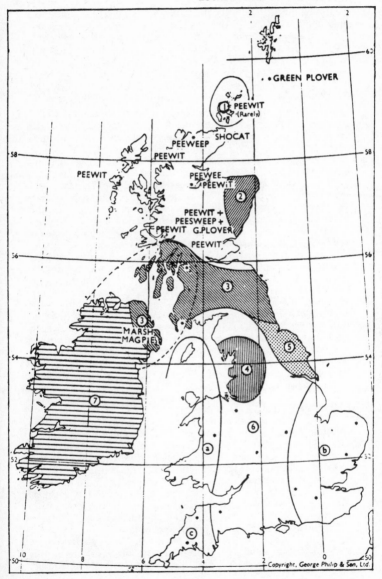

been mentioned. For birds, we cannot do better than look at the map (map 7) of the lapwing's local names. This is one of the few pieces of research done on bird-names, and its author, Mr K. G. Spencer, also carried out a survey of Lancashire bird-names (see *Journal of the Lancashire Dialect Society* 14, 1965); this, in turn, was inspired by Mr J. C. Maycock's similar survey in Yorkshire (see *Transactions of the Yorkshire Dialect Society*, Parts 53, 54, 56, 1953-6). A nationwide survey of bird-names is urgently needed.

We take as an illuminating example of local variation in plant-names the old titles of the bindweed. Apart from *bindweed* and *bind*, which are of general occurrence, *convulvulus* occupies much of the north (down to North Yorkshire) and a long strip of country comprising west Lancashire and Merseyside, most of Cheshire and Salop, while *ground-ivy* occupies another well-defined area in the south-west consisting of Cornwall and Devon except for the south-east. Throughout the rest of the country, names ending in *-bind* or *-wind* (*-vine* in west Suffolk, Cambridgeshire, Bedfordshire and Hertfordshire) predominate: *with(y)-wind* and *bith(y)-*, *bes-*, *beth-*, *beddy-*, *betty-wind* in most of the south, also *bell-wind* and *willy-wind*, a very large east-midland area of *cornbind*, stretching from Humberside and South and West Yorkshire to Buckinghamshire, two areas of *bear-bind* — one in the west, bordering on the *convulvulus* area, and one in the south-east (parts of Kent and East Sussex) — and an area of *bell-bind* in Essex and south Suffolk. There are besides these a good many other local names — *morning glory, wandering-willy, robin-run-the-dike*, and so on — and, as with other plants, much folklore probably underlies such local names as *devil's-gut, -nightcap, -twine* in the north of England. The names for the couch-grass, goose-grass, charlock, colt's-foot (see fig. 5), cowslip, daisy and dandelion are also of interest from both dialectal and folklore points of view — as are doubtless others.

Children's words

A most interesting class of words are those used specifically by children. Some of these receive attention in Iona and Peter Opie's *The Lore and Language of Schoolchildren*, from which the examples here are taken. The expressions they recorded may have social distributions which cut across the regional ones, e.g. the same word for various notions might perhaps be found in public — but no other types of — schools in places as far apart as Manchester and Oxford. The words, too, seem to cross easily from one region to another, and even from one social class to another, resulting in a complex mixture of vocabulary.

Of the large number of words for **gaining possession** of something, *bags* is in general use and probably best-known, plus *bagsy* and *baggy mine*. The north-west (old West Riding,

Fig. 5. The *colt's-foot* or *foal's-foot*. Other names: *cleat(s), mugwort, batterdock, cankerweed, cock's-foot, coosil, dishilago*. Here reproduced from Leonard Fuch's herbal *De Historia Stirpium* (1542).

Lancashire, Cheshire) favours *ballow that* or *I ballows that, barley me that* and *I bollars* or *bollar me; ferry* also emerges in the old West Riding, *fogs* or *fog it* and *jigs it* in Manchester and elsewhere in the west midlands; *nab it, nag it, pike I* or *prior pike* are all west-midland terms too, and there are many others: note, e.g., *cogs* or *coggy* from Bury St Edmunds, *shigs* from Bishop Auckland.

Bags and many of the rest of these are also used for **getting first place,** the most distinctive terms being found in the north: from Stoke-on-Trent to Lincoln and from Lincoln northwards on the eastern side of the Pennines, the operative word — in various pronunciations — is *foggy* (*I'm foggy* means 'I have the right to be first'), while *laggy* means that the last place is wanted. *Ferry* prevails in the towns of the old West Riding — Bradford, Halifax, Huddersfield — the dividing line between *foggy* and *ferry* apparently running through Sheffield, Barnsley, Wakefield and Leeds. *Ferry* appears again in Furness and Cumbria, but *firsy* in Lancashire.

Perhaps the most crucial word in a schoolchild's lexicon is his **truce term,** used, sometimes with a sign such as crossing fingers or feet, to gain temporary relief from some boisterous activity, fighting or the like. The Opies' map of these words shows large areas of *skinch, kings* or *kings and crosses* in the east and of *barley* (adjoining) in the west, with *fainites* in the south-east and south-west, these large regions being penetrated by other, different, words: in the east (north to south) by *keys, croggie, screams, scores, croggies, scrogs,* with *boosey, scruces, exes* in East Anglia, and the large area of *fainites* in London and the Home Counties being pierced by *bruises, cruces* and *scruce;* in the west (north to south) by *keys, blobs, crogs, screase, nicks,* with *cree* and *cruce* on the south Wales border and *cruces, creases* in the Gloucestershire/Oxfordshire area. The south-west has *crease, bars(y), scrames* and *screams,* all occurring in a preponderantly *fainites* area, while the area between this and the south-eastern *fainites* area is filled in with *scribs* — *scrases, screens* and *creams, scrames* and *screams* also occurring. An especially interesting general point which emerged from the Opies' work was that urban children's usage may differ from that of the surrounding countryside; e.g. Lincoln city gave *screams,* while the rest of Lincolnshire was mainly *kings* or *kings and crosses.* There is, throughout the country, however, much mixing.

Spoil-sports and the like have a variety of names applied to them up and down the country, but a specially interesting one is shown on map 8: *mardy* is used in the first instance of a spoilt (i.e. 'marred') child, and then, more generally, of a peevish or moody child; thirdly of a 'soft' child or cry-baby.

To take a final example, the Opies found that **sweets** are referred to by the younger generation as *comforters, goodies, sucks* or *suckers* and *quenchers,* also as *candies* (in Cleethorpes), and always as *spice* in the old West Riding. They felt (this was in 1959) that *lollies* was also becoming a general term.

A comparison with information given by the elderly informants of the Leeds Survey of English Dialects round about the 1950s is revealing here. According to them, *comforters* and *quenchers* were unknown, *goodies* was a common term, though mainly found in Humberside, North Yorkshire and north Cumbria, *sucks* and *suckers* were midland terms, *candy* was given in Lincolnshire (though further south than the Opies found it), *spice* (locally *spahs*) in the old West Riding area, but *lollies* — with about a

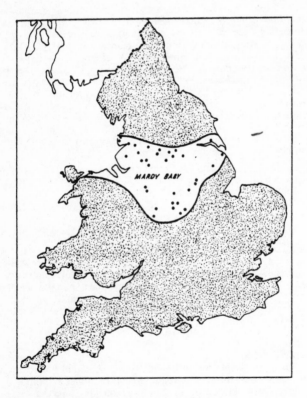

Map 8. The *mardy* area.

dozen examples — only in north Northamptonshire, Oxfordshire, west Buckinghamshire, east Wiltshire, north Hampshire and west Surrey. Has *lollies* spread from this area, or is its rise in popularity rather due to that of the 'lolly'-type sweet itself?

4. A look at history

To study English dialects without also studying their history deprives one of the perspective which tells us so much about their present condition. We shall now turn back to have a brief look at this.

The beginnings

The history of English begins when the Angles, Saxons and Jutes (also some Frisians) invaded Britain from the continental lowlands in the fifth century (although some were here much earlier), finding a population of Romanised Britons (Celts), and began to establish their kingdoms. Whether or not there were dialectal differences in their language even at the continental stage we do not know, but the Anglo-Saxon manuscripts which have come down to us from the eighth century onwards reveal several different *written* dialects (from which we can make inferences about the spoken language of the time), corresponding to the three Germanic tribes (above) mentioned by the Venerable Bede — a prime source — as having taken part in the invasions, namely:

1. Anglian, comprising (a) Northumbrian — found north of the river Humber as far as the Firth of Forth, and (b) Mercian — found between the Humber and the Thames.
2. West Saxon — found south of the Thames except for the region covered by —
3. Kentish — spoken by the Jutish colonists in Kent.

Of these, West Saxon is most fully represented in writing and was ultimately adopted as a standard literary dialect. These dialects form the basis of English, even as we know it today, and the roots of both present-day Standard English and the regional dialects are to be found here, although later history, as we shall see, has also had a large part to play. This 'Old English' period is usually regarded as lasting from the time of the first Anglo-Saxon writings (*c.* 700) up to about 1100 or 1150.

Celtic survival

During the Anglo-Saxon period groups of Britons remained, not only in western retreats, but scattered throughout England, their survival being evidenced by Anglo-Saxon law, river-names, and place-names such as Walcott, Walden and Walton which often contain the element *walh* 'foreigner, Welshman'. There may be evidence for the survival of Celtic dialects in the west of England until the ninth or tenth centuries, and in Cornwall the west of the county was Cornish-speaking until after 1500. As we have seen, some of the few Celtic words found in present-day English dialect — *bratt, brock,* also *ass* (ultimately from Latin) — derive from this early period.

The Scandinavians

Later in the Anglo-Saxon period another group of peoples began to have a much more decisive effect on both England and its language, namely the Scandinavians. The invasions of these barbarian peoples, mainly Norwegians and Danes, first struck England at the end of the eighth century. Later — by the second half of the ninth century — many of them began to settle more permanently, and by the eleventh century considerable integration of the two peoples — who during this period were mutually comprehensible in speech — had taken place.

The invaders came along two main routes: Danes (and some Swedes) sailed straight across the North Sea to Yorkshire and the east midlands; Norwegians arrived by way of the north of Scotland, settling in Shetland, Orkney, the Western Isles, the north of Ireland and the Isle of Man, from where they established permanent colonies in north-west England, especially in Cumbria and north Lancashire.

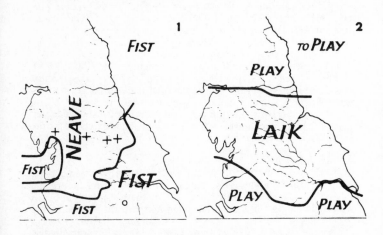

Map 9. Two more Scandinavian words: *neave* 'fist', *laik* 'play'. Key (for 'fist'): + *fist,* o *neave.*

The only serious resistance to the Scandinavian attacks came from King Alfred, who defeated the Danes led by Guthrum in Wiltshire and then made peace with him in 878 by the Treaty of Wedmore. Under its terms England was divided, sovereignty over the region north and east of the old (Roman) Watling Street, stretching from London to Chester, being assigned to Guthrum, leaving London and the south and west to Alfred. A final period of attack, between 990 and 1016, resulted in the deposition of Ethelred the Unready and the succession of King Svein of Denmark, followed by his son, the great Canute, with whose reign Scandinavian attacks came to an end.

At first, Scandinavian words in English are few — only some eighty are to be detected in writings earlier than 1150, fairly common words like *egg* (verb), *husband, law, take* and *wrong*. However, by the thirteenth century many more appear in the extant documents, especially in those from the north and east midlands, doubtless having been adopted into spoken English in Anglo-Saxon times. Again, these are commonplace words like *both, dirt, ill, though* and *wing*.

Many Scandinavian words found their way only into northern and east-midland vernacular and survived there from Middle English times up to the nineteenth century or, in some cases, the present day. Many were mentioned in Chapter 2, but we may add the following: *blae-berry* 'bilberry' (ON *blá* 'blue' + OE *berige*), *drucken* 'drunken' (ON *drukkinn*), *feal* 'hide' (ON *fela*), *gaumless* 'stupid' (ON *gaumr* + OE *læs*), *grain* 'branch' (ON *greinn*), *lait* 'seek' (ON *leita*), *laik* 'play' (ON *leika*), *rawk* 'mist' (Old Scandinavian *•raukr*), *skell(-boose)* 'partition in cow-house' (cf. ON *skilja* 'divide' + OE *•bōs*). Neither should we forget that there may have been a certain phonetic influence.

The pattern of Scandinavian settlement — to the east of Watling Street and in the counties of the north-west (Lancashire and Cumbria) — suggests that the area of loan-words (see map 3) was originally somewhat more extensive than at present, their modern northern distribution being only a relic of this once larger area which, as place-name evidence tells us, once extended as far south as south Essex.

French influence

What we call the Middle English period is regarded as covering 1100 or 1150 to about 1450. About a hundred years before the beginning of this era the Norman Conquest brought about a decline in English literary production and also the demise of the West Saxon dialect as a standard literary dialect. English literature now came to be written in a wide variety of forms up and down the country and had also to contend with Anglo-Norman, a dialect of French developed on English soil as a second literary and official language. In the fourteenth century, however, English reappeared as the sole language of literature and of social and legal institutions, becoming increasingly used in literature and gradually being reinstated in all official spheres — courts, schools, universities and parliament.

Although — at least at the beginning — the French aristocracy had spoken only French, the English peasants meanwhile continuing with their native tongue, perhaps by the twelfth to thirteenth centuries many, if not most, nobles were bilingual, while there were also bilingual middle classes of both English and French, and this ultimately led to the extinction of French in England: once the conquerors had become merely a bilingual upper class, the way was open for the loss of the less useful 'upper' language and the reinstatement of the 'lower' (i.e. English).

While French was the dominant language, however, there had been much borrowing of French words into English, in both its spoken and written forms: words like *abbey, aunt, blanket, crown, jewel, stranger, tune, veal* — an estimated ten thousand or so by 1500, with more in later years. Some of these, in dialect, we had cause to mention earlier — *launder* 'gutter', *urchin* 'hedgehog', *tumble* etc 'farmcart', *court* 'farmyard', *mommet* 'scarecrow'. Neither must we forget the French element which emerged into the English dialect of west Cornwall via Cornish.

To these, however, we could add a great many more, e.g.: (Lincolnshire and Humberside) *cow-stable* (OE *cū* + OF *estable*); (Wiltshire) *vault* 'well, earth-closet' (OF *voute, volte*); (Cornwall) *planching* 'upstairs floor' (ultimately from Fr *planche* 'plank'); (south Devon) *causen* floor, 'flagged' floor (ONF *caucie* + *-en*); (northern and north-midland) *tunnel* 'funnel' (OF *tonel*); (south-western) *rummage* 'rubbish' (Fr *arrumage*); (south-western) *flask, flasket* 'clothes-basket' (OF *flasque, flasquet*) and *maund* 'feeding-basket' (for animals) (OF *mande*); (northern and midland) *bonny* 'pretty' (perhaps OF *bon*), and many more.

Other foreign contacts

France was England's chief foreign contact during and subsequent to the Middle Ages, but there was also intimate contact with the Low Countries from a very early date: the Flemish and Dutch had major roles in such English enterprises as weaving, sheep-rearing and the wool trade in Kent, market-gardening and fruit growing in the same county, engineering work in Dover harbour and the glass-making industry. There has also been a close connection between English and continental fishing communities, and further intercourse arose from sixteenth-century religious persecution on the Continent, when there was an influx of refugees to this country.

Loan-words from these sources are, although fewer than those from France, well-known in Standard English, e.g. *hop* (noun), *kit, skipper, slim,* perhaps *hoist* and *pack* and numerous others. And the dialects contain some further examples; to *spile, spill, splint* 'splinter' and *pad* 'path' one could add: (Devon) *brandis* 'gridiron' (cf. Du *brandijzer* 'branding-iron'); (widespread) *groop* 'drain in cow-house' (MDu *groepe*); (Northumberland and north Cumbrian) *keek* 'peep' (perhaps MDu *kieken* or LG *kîken*); (midlands and south-eastern) *snap* 'snack' (MDu or MLG *snappen*); (East Anglian) *stull* 'large piece of anything edible', e.g. bread (perhaps Frisian *stulle* 'piece, lump'); (south Devon, east and central Cornwall) *fitch* 'polecat' (early Du *fisse, visse, vitsche*). We may add, too, words from fishermen's dialect such as *lugger* (cf. Du *logger*) and *yawl* (apparently MLG *jolle* or Du *jol*), both names of small boats, *spill* 'shank of anchor' (apparently the same word as *spill* 'splinter'). Flemish influence may also be responsible for south-eastern **d** in *that, there, these,* etc (see page 27).

There has also been contact with Germany since the Middle Ages, especially in the field of mining, and some loan-words from this source are perhaps to be found, but contacts with Italy, Spain and Portugal have given us very few words which are specifically dialectal.

Standard English

As we have seen, in the fourteenth century English reasserted itself in social and literary spheres, and from this time English writings appear in numerous literary genres and a large number of different dialects — Kentish, Lincolnshire, Yorkshire, west-midland, Gloucestershire, London, Norfolk and a great many more. It is important to realise that at this time *all* English was dialectal: there was no one 'standard' form, spoken or written, but a large number of local ways of writing and speaking — 'local standards', as one might call them.

Out of this variety of local forms one in particular began to rise to pre-eminence, first in writing and then also in speech. This was an *upper-class* dialect developed in London in the fourteenth and fifteenth centuries mainly on the basis of the influential dialect of immigrants to the capital from the east midlands. From this time on, dialect characteristics began to disappear in both writings intended for the public and those of a private nature (diaries, letters, etc), while 'London' English became more and more the predominant form, being used for all purposes by educated men of every region. By the end of the seventeenth century most of the surviving variations in writing had gone, and there was more or less one norm.

In speech we have no direct evidence for a standard until much later, though we generally assume that a spoken standard arose not long after the written standard. But in 1589 the author of *The*

NORTHERN

WEST MIDLAND

EAST MIDLAND

SOUTH-WESTERN

SOUTH-EASTERN

0 ——— 100 MLS.

Map 10. Middle English dialects. The classification is necessarily a rough one pending further research.

Arte of English Poesie advised poets to adopt 'the usual speech of the Court, and that of London and the shires lying about London within sixty miles', and this is only one of a number of statements to the effect that educated, upper-class London and southern speech was by this time the model for those who wanted their speech to be of the 'best' sort. Provincialisms were ridiculed as barbaric by the seventeenth-century grammarians, and on the stage rustic speakers were given broad west-country dialects to emphasise their lowly status. As 'Standard English' rose in favour, so non-Standard types declined.

At first, however, early Standard English was reasonably free in its permission of variants in pronunciation and grammar, but the eighteenth century saw a movement towards uniformity in both. 'For pronunciation', stated Dr Johnson, 'the best general rule is to consider those as the most elegant speakers who deviate least from the written word.' Since this time, aided by the massive swing from rural to urban living which has taken place since the first half of the nineteenth century, the rise of public schools and later the BBC, variants in pronunciation (and indeed at all levels) have gradually disappeared and a Standard English based on the influential written standard has taken their place.

In the days before the growth of towns and their suburbs the patterning of English dialects was in the main geographical, but afterwards another patterning came more to the fore, namely a social one. In the towns, speech varieties classified themselves not on a geographical but on a social basis, in which the speech of non-dialect speakers emerged at the top of a scale of linguistic values, that of the speakers of the local form of speech at the bottom.

The fate of the regional dialects

In the countryside, meanwhile, the old rural dialects continued but were subject to a constant tendency towards modification in the direction of Standard English. In many areas, because of their comparative isolation, e.g. the Yorkshire Dales, rural Devon, this type of speech has been preserved remarkably well, although most dialect speakers are 'bi-dialectal' — they speak the local dialect within their own community but easily switch to Standard English for the benefit of outsiders or when away from their own home. Thomas Hardy captured this state of affairs well in *Tess of the d'Urbervilles* (1891), when he wrote:

> Mrs Durbeyfield habitually spoke the dialect; her daughter, who had passed the Sixth Standard in the National School under a London-trained mistress, spoke two languages: the dialect at home, more or less; ordinary English abroad and to persons of quality.

The present situation

In the countryside, then, much regional dialect remains, especially among the older people, although this is (as it has been for some hundreds of years) in a state of constant erosion by Standard English, especially as it is passed down to the new generations. Clearly, however, the extent to which the local dialect is eliminated differs from region to region and from family to family. In some areas it may be total, whereas in others the children and young people may possess and hand on the dialect in a reasonably good state of preservation. It is in the larger towns that we best see the social hierarchy referred to above, where there co-exist people with no dialect at all and people with the very marked dialect of the region, and in between a multiplicity of varieties — part regional, part non-regional. Recently there has emerged a new respect for regional dialect, but mainly in intellectual quarters. The reasons given for this are complex, but the chief of them — stated baldly — is that any type of speech is as adequate for communication as any other.

Dialect literature

People had been conscious of the existence of regional varieties of English from the fourteenth century onwards; they received attention from archaising poets like Edmund Spenser, from the antiquarians of the sixteenth and seventeenth centuries (Leland, Norden, Camden, Sir Thomas Browne) and from the grammarians of the sixteenth to eighteenth centuries. But from at least the seventeenth century on there were attempts to compile glossaries of local dialect and to write dialect poems, dialogues and other works, both to display the characteristic features of these moribund forms of speech and to preserve them from extinction. With the nineteenth century this was done on a more scientific and systematic basis, and dialect study was pursued — and has been ever since — with the aim of illuminating the history of the English language as a whole. Outstanding examples of such writers were the glossarists John Ray (1627-1705) and Francis Grose (c. 1731-91) — older glossaries are still of use in the investigation of the now obsolete vocabularies of different regions — the Yorkshireman George Meriton, who (c. 1683) wrote *A Yorkshire Dialogue,* in which he adapted the alphabet to express the sounds of the contemporary Yorkshire dialect, and the author of the *Exmoor Courtship* and *Exmoor Scolding,* Devonshire dialogues of just over three hundred lines each, first contributed to *The Gentleman's Magazine* in 1746.

During the nineteenth century dialect literature of this type flourished everywhere, but especially in the north of England, perhaps because, as Professor Brook says, it satisfied the needs of the new industrial communities then coming into existence. Here dialect writing still flourishes today, both under the auspices of the dialect societies and independently in the form of collections of dialect verse and contributions to journals.

5. Literary dialect

We must distinguish the dialect literature mentioned in the last chapter from 'literary dialect', i.e. the use of dialectal forms of speech for literary purposes. The latter has a long tradition in English literature, ranging from some 'northern' dialogue written by Chaucer for 'The Reeve's Tale' (end of the fourteenth century) to D. H. Lawrence's Nottinghamshire dialogues in *Lady Chatterley's Lover* (1928). This literary dialect consists of passages of verse or prose designed to give colour to an author's work by imitating characteristics of speech, regional and social. In addition, some writers, like William Barnes and Tennyson, have written complete poems in dialect. Here there is room for one representative sample only; let us consider the following passage:

> 'I said I was as good as anybody else in the world, din't I?' Arthur demanded. 'And I mean it. Do you think if I won the football pools I'd gi' yo' a penny on it? Or gi' anybody else owt? Not likely. I'd keep it all mysen, except for seeing my family right. I'd buy 'em a house and set 'em up for life, but anybody else could whistle for it. I've 'eard that blokes as win football pools get thousands o' beggin' letters, but yer know what I'd do if I got 'em? I'll tell yer what I'd do: I'd mek a bonfire on 'em.'

This is an extract from Alan Sillitoe's novel *Saturday Night and Sunday Morning*, published in 1958. In it the author aims to give a rough idea of the Nottingham dialect — note regional items like *yo'* 'you', *owt* 'anything', *mysen* 'myself', *mek* 'make', which are characteristic of the area. But by far the greater number of the features we can observe are not specially regional but merely non-standard. Note *din't, gi'*, 'a penny on it', 'a bonfire on 'em', *'em*, 'set 'em up' and 'whistle for it' (slang expressions), *'eard* (h- lost), *as* 'who', *o'*, *beggin'*, *yer*. These — showing loss of various consonants, substandard expressions and the like — are ubiquitous. There is thus a mixture, intending to give an impression both of local dialect and general substandard English, but without being incomprehensible. This type of dialect dialogue is a far cry from the efforts of Emily Bronte in *Wuthering Heights* and Bernard Shaw in *Captain Brassbound's Conversion*, who made serious attempts to reconstruct the sound-system of the dialects they were imitating, namely North Yorkshire and Cockney respectively.

Dialect on the stage, radio and television

Even from before the Elizabethan period there were attempts in plays to suggest regional dialect — the most notable being the use of a southern or south-western dialect to represent the common speech of the clod-hopping country yokel — although the playwrights tended not to give the dialect in any great detail, but left it to the performers to bring it alive from such indications as *cham* 'ich (i.e. I) am', *vell* 'fell', *zome* 'some'. As Shakespeare's Edgar says in *King Lear* (act IV, scene 6):

Chill not let go Zir, without vurther 'casion!

'I will not let go, sir, without further occasion' (i.e. cause).

In *Henry IV* and *Henry V*, Shakespeare's Mistress Quickly also provides an example of stage Cockney, a type which then disappears until the middle of the eighteenth century. Shaw's Drinkwater in *Captain Brassbound's Conversion* (1899) is a notable example of detailed Cockney speech for the stage. It is unusual, however, for modern playwrights to represent stage dialect in such great detail as Shaw did and more customary for any dialect speech required to be assumed by the actor himself.

In the twentieth century literary dialect has been extended to radio and television, and considerable effort is made nowadays when producing, for example, a play based on a novel by D. H. Lawrence to get the characters to speak an accurate regional and social dialect, without becoming unintelligible, not always easily achieved with the broader dialects.

In particular, there has been in recent years a growth of interest in the industrial north-east and its past and present social problems. This means that the dialect of the area, especially that of the working-class, has had to be reproduced on a large scale. Actors who are themselves natives of the area are frequently employed, and to good effect. One recent series of this type was impressive in marking the social differences between management (speaking 'modified regional dialect') and workers (with broad regional dialect).

There are a good many situation comedies whose characters need a dialect for humorous purposes. One of the most famous of recent years has been *Till Death us do Part*, centred round the voluble Alf Garnett and his family and set in east London. Here the dialect was completely genuine, with *bloody, nut, funny*, etc, pronounced as a near-**a** sound, 'glottalisation' of **t** (*wa'er* 'water', etc), the substitution of **th** by **f** and **dh** by **v** (*Smif* 'smith', *bruvver* 'brother'), and a proliferation of *ain't*s and other non-RSE grammatical forms.

To take another example, *The Liver Birds*, centred round two

Liverpool girls, also managed to capture 'modified Liverpudlian' in a genuinely convincing way, and other northern (Lancashire, Yorkshire) situation comedies are too numerous to mention. But again, all such series greatly benefit from the employment of actors and actresses who are themselves natives of the area concerned.

Individual English comedians frequently rely on either a Yorkshire/Lancashire voice or Cockney (but note Pam Ayres, with the reverted **r** and vowels of rural Buckinghamshire!). The comedian with an exaggerated upper-class voice is not as popular as he was, and regional dialect once more holds the stage. This perhaps coincides with a period in which RSE is not so much in the ascendant as a prestigious type of spoken English.

Some works containing literary dialect

G. Chaucer, 'The Reeve's Tale' in *The Canterbury Tales* (*c.* 1390; northern); early plays *Respublica* (*c.* 1553) and *Gammer Gurton's Needle* (*c.* 1560; both south-western); Edmund Spenser, *The Shepheardes Calendar* (1579; mainly northern and archaic); W. Shakespeare, *King Lear* (first printing 1608; act IV, some south-western); Ben Jonson, *A Tale of a Tub* (1596/7; south-western), *The Sad Shepherd* (first printing 1641; northern); works of the poets John Clare (1793-1864; Northamptonshire); Tennyson (1802-92; Lincolnshire dialect poems); William Barnes (1801-86; Dorset); Thomas Hardy (1840-1928; 'Wessex'); R. Kipling, *Barrack-Room Ballads* (1889-91; Cockney); novels of Hardy (above); George Eliot (1819-80; Warwickshire); E. Bronte (1818-48; North Yorkshire); C. Dickens (1812-70; Yorkshire, Lancashire, East Anglia); D. H. Lawrence (1885-1930; Nottinghamshire); and, more recently, the writers Thomas Armstrong, Phyllis Bentley, J. B. Priestley, John Braine, Alan Sillitoe, Stan Barstow (all northern). See also G. B. Shaw, *Captain Brassbound's Conversion* (1899; Cockney).

6. The study of dialect

Dialect study in England

Serious dialect study in England was prompted by the publication of German and French dialect work begun at the end of the last century. The English Dialect Society was founded in 1873, with the intention of collecting words from the regional dialects for an English dialect dictionary. These were published in numerous volumes, and all the material was later assembled, and a great deal more added, by Joseph Wright, Professor of Comparative Philology at Oxford, in the famous *English Dialect Dictionary* and *English Dialect Grammar* (1898-1905).

In the field of pronunciation, A. J. Ellis had by this time published a huge work *On Early English Pronunciation, Part V: The Existing Phonology of English Dialects* (1889).

In the present century the *Survey of English Dialects* (*SED;* 1962-71) was initiated by Harold Orton and Eugen Dieth at Leeds University in 1946 and, based on the answers to a lengthy questionnaire, provides a body of material relating to pronunciation, vocabulary and grammar from elderly people in

Fig. 6. Gunnerside 'Gunnar's pasture' (ON **Gunnarr** + **saetr**) in Swaledale. Dialect work for the Survey of English Dialects was carried out in the area.

313 (nearly all rural) localities in England. Together with the *Word Geography of England* (1974) and the more recent (1978) *Linguistic Atlas of England* — both based upon *SED* — it gives a unique description of traditional regional English dialect of the middle of this century. There are also tape-recordings from every locality, which are housed in the archives of Leeds University's Institute of Dialect and Folk Life Studies (founded in 1964).

Similar work, though based on different methods and emerging in a different form of presentation, is being done in the Survey of Anglo-Welsh Dialects at the University College of Swansea, the Linguistic Survey of Scotland (whose first two volumes are now in print in map form) at the University of Edinburgh, and surveys of Ulster dialects at Queen's University, Belfast, and the New University of Ulster at Coleraine.

Since 1964 Sheffield University has had a Centre for English Cultural Tradition and Language, which collects material on all aspects of language and cultural traditions throughout the British Isles, as a basic resource for research, and has assembled a substantial body of data on regional and social dialects, slang, occupational vocabulary, proverbs and sayings, together with information on local and traditional customs and beliefs; the Survey also sponsors and directs many projects in the field of children's language and folklore. In particular, it is conducting an investigation of traditional verbal constraints used by adults in controlling the behaviour of children.

Traditional dialectology — 'linguistic geography' — has been mainly concerned with old regional dialect, in an attempt to shed light on the history of the English language by examining the old forms of words, but language has also a social dimension: as we have said, there is variation in speech between people of different classes as much as there is between people from different areas. Some scholars have, therefore, turned their attention to the sound systems found in urban dialects, to try to reveal this social linguistic 'stratification', since towns house large populations of different classes. This research, therefore, does not seek to elicit regional variation in the speech of one sector of the community only (i.e. the elderly section) but is concerned with variation between different sectors and classes as a result of social and economic causes.

Some guidelines for collecting dialect

Future research into dialects may well continue to concentrate on towns, since much work remains to be done on places as different as Birmingham and Canterbury, Harrogate and Northampton. This complex task, which needs training and experience, is on the whole best left to the experts, though there is no reason why vocabulary should not be collected in these places by serious amateurs.

There is more hope for the serious amateur in the field of traditional dialectology (including occupational dialect), and he might well begin by joining one of the dialect societies in order to be in contact with people of similar interests. A list is given at the end of this book.

Traditional dialect work is something like research into local history, which informed amateurs have undertaken for some time. But the *informed* is important! Mere odd-word collecting only results in a private museum of unconnected items, of limited interest. No dialect item is of value unless it is known *exactly where* it was picked up, *who* said it, and *when* it was collected.

Background research

Whatever aim one has, some reading about the history of the English language and the area (industry, etc) under scrutiny is always useful. If an area, have a look especially at the place-names with a reliable guide-book, and a certain reconnoitring, getting to know the terrain and the sort of place it is, number of inhabitants and so on, is indispensable. If you are looking for the oldest stratum of the dialect, you will have to go to the remotest villages and interview the oldest people there. If an industry or children's language is being investigated, you will probably go to a factory or school.

Informants

The important thing, however, is to find your informants (perhaps through the agency of friends and relatives, shopkeepers, local clergy, schoolteachers or librarians) — not casually sit around jotting down random words you may hear. You should find out your informant's name and address, age, place of birth and that of his parents, education, and how long he has spent in the district and in his occupation. Unless you are deliberately studying people of 'mixed pedigrees', it is important to select informants who have been natives of the district concerned since their early childhood, for speech habits begin early and someone who has lived up to the age of, say, eighteen in a nearby village might well have speech habits which really belong to a completely different dialect — perhaps on the other side of an important dialect boundary! So 'native residence' is crucial. If his family have been natives for hundreds of years, so much the better.

Informants should be willing to help and sound in wind and limb. Deaf people and those with speech defects may prove unsuitable. People who do not speak dialect but only imitate it are *always* unsuitable — the information must be got at first hand, from genuine dialect speakers.

57

Place of interview

This should be a quiet place — preferably the informant's own home, where he will feel most at ease. Pubs, contrary to popular opinion, are not the place for dialect surveys. Assume the role of pupil, with your informant as teacher: you need information — he can provide it.

Questions and responses

The answers you are seeking from your informant and the method of getting them will again depend on the sort of information you require. Sounds — phonology — need careful handling and without phonetic and philological training are better left to the experts. Vocabulary and grammar are more straight-forward fields.

Dialect surveys have usually been carried out by questionnaire — a list of questions which, when put to an informant, will reveal by the answers received the essential components of his sound-system, vocabulary and grammar. You may use an existing questionnaire, like the well-known Dieth-Orton one, most carefully compiled for the Survey of English Dialects, or, perhaps better, you may compile your own, briefer version, specifically geared to what you are looking for. Pictures and diagrams (e.g. of parts of machinery — agricultural or industrial) are sometimes useful.

Questions should be either straightforward, like 'What do you call this?' (putting your tongue out), or completing ones, like 'The place where you store your hay is called . . . ?', which the informant will then complete. But never say 'What do you call the hay-loft?' or the informant will simply say 'hay-loft' — your question has already suggested it to him. As a *very last* resort, however, you can say 'Would you ever call it a *tallet, shippon, mow-hay, linhay* (etc)?' Preferably record the answer in its context, e.g. 'We sometimes call that a . . .', and note also any 'incidental material' — remarks interspersed with the answers, e.g. 'That's slang' or 'My dad used to call it . . .'

In place of the questionnaire method some investigators now prefer to make a longish tape-recording for future analysis. This is all right, except that you may not get all the information you require. Best of all, perhaps, if time permits, is questionnaire *plus* tape-recording. The latter could usefully include details of the informant's early life, methods of hedging or pig-killing, local anecdotes and so on. This should provide useful information additional to that elicited by the questionnaire.

Historical dialect

Investigating historical dialect is a more solitary occupation. Post-medieval documents such as account-books and inventories may reveal numerous local words (and suggest their pronunciations — but great care, and training, are needed here) for implements, tools and household goods, for even though dialects were starting to break down, local words are still quite frequent in such sources, and pursuing them is a fascinating and worthwhile occupation.

Some institutions with active dialect interests

Institute of Dialect and Folk Life Studies, the University, Leeds (archives of dialect dissertations, tape-recordings, etc). Curator: Professor T. Shippey.

Survey of Tyneside Speech, Department of English, the University, Newcastle-upon-Tyne.

Centre for English Cultural Tradition and Language, the University, Sheffield (see page 56; biennial journal: *Lore and Language*). Director: Dr J. D. A. Widdowson.

Institute of Cornish Studies, Trevenson House, Pool, Redruth. Director: Professor A. C. Thomas.

Yorkshire Dialect Society (aims: to encourage interest in and the study of Yorkshire dialect speech and literature and kindred subjects; annual *Transactions* and *Summer Bulletin*). Secretary: Mr G. Williams, Fieldhead House, West Street, Hoyland, Barnsley, S74 9AG.

Lancashire Dialect Society (aims: the fostering of the study of northern English dialects and their preservation in speech and writing; annual *Journal*, summer *Newsletter*). Secretary: Mr Bob Dyson, 3 Staining Rise, Staining, Blackpool.

Lakeland Dialect Society (aims: to encourage dialect writing and foster interest in dialect at both academic and 'human' levels; annual *Journal*). Secretary: Miss N. Dawson, 8 Barras Close, Morton Park, Carlisle, CA2 6PR.

Federation of Old Cornwall Societies (biennial journal: *Old Cornwall*). Secretary: Miss J. Rendell, MBE, Tremarsh, Launceston. Dialect recorder: Miss D. Drake, 19 Higher Pumpfield Row, Pool, Redruth.

Linguistic Survey of Scotland, the University, Edinburgh.

Survey of Anglo-Welsh Dialects, Department of English, University College of Swansea. Director: Mr D. Parry.

Tape-recorded Survey of Hiberno-English Speech. Directors: Mr G. B. Adams, Ulster Folk and Transport Museum; Mr M. V. Barry, Queen's University of Belfast; Mr P. M. Tilling, New University of Ulster, Coleraine.

Ulster Folk and Transport Museum, Belfast. Dialect Archivist: Mr G. B. Adams.

Further reading

General works

English Dialects. G. L. Brook. 2nd ed., Deutsch, 1965.

English Dialects: An Introduction. M. F. Wakelin. 2nd. ed., Athlone Press, 1977.

The English Language in Modern Times. M. Schlauch. Warsaw, distributed outside Poland by OUP, 1959.

A History of the English Language. A. C. Baugh and T. Cable. 3rd ed., Routledge, 1978.

Varieties of English. G. L. Brook. Macmillan, 1973.

Regional and social dialect

Accents of English. J. C. Wells. Cambridge University Press, 1982. (Vol. 2 on the British Isles.)

Broad Norfolk. Jonathan Mardle. Wensum Books (Norwich), 1973.

Cockney Dialect and Slang. Peter Wright. Batsford, 1981.

Cockney Past and Present. W. Matthews. Routledge, 1938.

Dialectology. J. K. Chambers and P. Trudgill. Cambridge University Press, 1980. (Quite theoretical.)

Dialects in the South-West of England: A Lexical Investigation. A. Fischer. Francke, Berne, 1976.

A Dictionary of the Sussex Dialect. W. D. Parish, revised H. Hall. Privately printed, 1957.

English Accents and Dialects. A. Hughes and P. Trudgill. Arnold, 1979. (Social and regional, but mainly urban. Accompanying tape).

English Dialect Dictionary. Joseph Wright. OUP, 1898-1905. (Bibliography lists the older glossaries.)

English Dialect Grammar. Joseph Wright. OUP, 1905.

English Dialect Society publications (1873-96).

An Introduction to a Survey of Scottish Dialects. A. McIntosh. Nelson, 1952.

Journal of the Lakeland Dialect Society.

Journal of the Lancashire Dialect Society.

Language and History in Cornwall. M. F. Wakelin. Leicester University Press, 1975.

Language in the British Isles. Edited by P. Trudgill. Cambridge University Press, 1984. (Comprehensive survey.)

Lincolnshire Dialect. G. E. Campion. Richard Kay (Boston), 1976.

Linguistic Atlas of England. H. Orton, S. Sanderson and J. D. A. Widdowson. Croom Helm, 1978.

Linguistic Atlas of Scotland. J. Y. Mather and H. Speitel. Vols. I and II, Croom Helm, 1975-7.

New Cambridge Bibliography of English Literature. Vol. I, ed. G. Watson. Cambridge University Press, 1974. (Columns 103-8 list glossaries, etc.)

A Northumberland and Durham Word Book. C. Geeson. Harold Hill (Newcastle), 1969.

On Early English Pronunciation, Part V. A. J. Ellis. Early English Text Society, Extra Series, 1889.

Patterns in the Folk Speech of the British Isles. M. F. Wakelin and others. Athlone Press, 1972. (See especially paper on Scots-Irish boundary in Ulster.)

Phonological Atlas of the Northern Region. E. Kolb. Francke, Berne, 1966.

The Scottish-English Linguistic Border: Lexical Aspects. B. Glauser. Francke, Berne, 1974.

The Social Differentiation of English in Norwich. P. Trudgill. Cambridge University Press, 1974.

Sociolinguistic Patterns in British English. P. Trudgill and others. Edward Arnold, 1978. (Papers on Belfast, Glasgow, Edinburgh, Liverpool, Bradford, Newcastle, Reading and East Anglia.)

Staffordshire Dialect Words: A Historical Survey. David Wilson. Moorland Publishing Company, 1974.

The Study of Dialect. K. M. Petyt. Deutsch, 1980. (Quite theoretical.)

The Suffolk Dialect of the Twentieth Century. A. O. D. Claxton. Norman Adlard (Ipswich), 1954.

Survey of Anglo-Welsh Dialects. D. Parry. Lithograph (obtainable from the author), 1977-.

Survey of English Dialects. H. Orton and others. E. J. Arnold, 1962-71.

Transactions of the Yorkshire Dialect Society.

Ulster Dialects: An Introductory Symposium. Ulster Folk Museum, 1964.

Varieties of English around the World: South-west England. M. F. Wakelin. Benjamin, Amsterdam, forthcoming (1986). (Accompanying tape.)

West-Country Words and Ways. K. Phillips. David and Charles, 1976. (Cornwall.)

A Word Geography of England. H. Orton and N. Wright. Seminar Press, 1974.

Yorkshire Dialects. John Waddington-Feather. Dalesman Publishing Company, 1970.

Reprints of older (nineteenth-century, early twentieth-century) works on the dialects of Buckinghamshire, Cheshire, Cumbria, Essex, Northamptonshire and Yorkshire (old West Riding) are available from E. P. Publishing Ltd, Wakefield.

Occupational and specialised dialects

A Dictionary of English Plant-Names. J. Britton and R. Holland. English Dialect Society, 1878-86.

A Dictionary of Rhyming Slang. J. Franklyn. Routledge, 1960.

A Dictionary of Sailors' Slang. W. Granville. Deutsch, 1962.

A Dictionary of the Underworld. E. Partridge. 3rd ed., Routledge, 1968.

A Glossary of Cornish Sea-Words. R. M. Nance, ed. P. A. S. Pool. Federation of Old Cornwall Societies, Marazion, 1963.

A Glossary of Devonshire Plant Names. H. Friend. English Dialect Society, 1882.

A Glossary of Railwaymen's Talk. F. McKenna. History Workshop Pamphlets, 1970.

The Language of British Industry. Peter Wright. Macmillan, 1974.

The Lapwing in Britain. K. G. Spencer. A. Brown and Sons (London and Hull), 1953.

Lore and Language. Sheffield; see especially Vol. 2, No. 1 (July 1974) on back-slang in Birmingham meat-trade.

The Lore and Language of Schoolchildren. I. and P. Opie. OUP, 1959.

Made in England. D. Hartley. 4th ed., Eyre Methuen, 1974.

Provincial Names and Folk Lore of British Birds. C. Swainson. English Dialect Society, 1885.

The Terminology of Fishing. W. Elmer. Francke, Berne, 1973.

They Don't Speak Our Language. S. Rogers and others. Edward Arnold, 1976. (On language of children and adolescents.)

Traditional Country Craftsmen. J. Geraint Jenkins. Routledge, 1965.

Literary dialect

Authors who have used dialect for special purposes are listed on page 54. Note also the anthologies:

A Lancashire Anthology. May Yates. Hodder and Stoughton, 1923.

The White Rose Garland of Yorkshire Dialect Verse and Local and Folk-Lore Rhymes. Ed. W. J. Halliday and A. S. Umpleby. Dent, 1949.

Further anthologies of verse published by the Yorkshire Dialect Society are available from the Librarian YDS, School of English, Leeds University.

Index

Titles in the 'Discovering' series with their series numbers

From your bookseller or from Shire Publications Ltd, Cromwell House, Church Street, Princes Risborough, Aylesbury, Bucks, HP17 9AJ, U.K.